Comprehension

Ages 9-10

Photocopiable skills activities

Authors Gordon Winch, Gregory Blaxell and Helena Rigby

Editor Dulcie Booth

Assistant editor Roanne Davis

Series designers Joy Monkhouse and Rachael Hammond

Designer Mark Udall

Cover illustration Gerald Hawksley

Illustrations Beverly Curl (pages 32, 36, 38, 40, 42, 44, 50, 56, 91–2, 94, 96, 100, 106, 108–10, 112, 114, 116, 118–20, 122), Ann Johns (pages 22, 24, 28, 52, 54, 58, 60, 62, 66, 68, 70, 72, 74, 76, 78, 80)

Designed using Adobe InDesign
Processed by Scholastic Ltd, Leamington Spa

Published by Scholastic Ltd, Villiers House, Clarendon Avenue, Leamington Spa, Warwickshire CV32 5PR

Printed by Bell & Bain Ltd, Glasgow

Adapted from original material entitled *Read Well* © Gordon Winch and Gregory Blaxell published by Martin Education of Horwitz House, 55 Chandos St, St Leonards 2065, NSW, Australia

Text on pages 22–81 © 1998 Gordon Winch and Gregory Blaxell
Text on pages 5-21, 91-128 © 1998 Helena Rigby
© 1998, 2002 Scholastic Ltd

5 6 7 8 9 0   5 6 7 8 9 0 1

British Library Cataloguing-in-Publication Data
A catalogue record for this book is available from the British Library.

ISBN 0439-98325-8

Introduction 5

Models of text genres 10

Assessment 18

Units

Poetry
1. Door 22
2. Too early 24
3. Big black bird 26
4. Me-moving 28

Narrative
5. Theseus slays the Minotaur 30
6. Lauren and the flying dog (1) 32
7. Lauren and the flying dog (2) 34
8. Androcles and the lion 36
9. The amazing Tamara Mudpuddle 38
10. The lion and the mouse 40
11. Julie of the Wolves 42
12. Tom 44

Drama
13. The Hare with many friends 46
14. The storm 48
15. Brer Rabbit and the tar baby 50

Recount
16. Our trip to Shingle Cove 52
17. Flat Stanley 54

Instructions
18. How to catch a train 56
19. How to grow tomatoes 58
20. Catching a fish 60

Report
21. Sports day 62
22. The elephant 64
23. The earthworm 66

Explanation
24. How a rainbow is made 68
25. How we digest our food 70
26. Why an iceberg floats 72
27. Why some spiders have webs 74

Argument
28. A varied diet is best 76
29. Team games are more fun 78
30. Cats make good pets 80

Answers to units 82

Supplementary units

Poetry
1. Thirty-two lengths 91
2. Cinderella 92
3. Grammar 94

Narrative
4. The story of Giant Kippernose 95
5. Cam Jansen and the mystery of the UFO 96
6. Dreams 98
7. The cave 100
8. Harry's Mad 102

Drama
9. The strange creature 103
10. The rescue 104

Recount
11. The Beatles 106
12. Swimming lessons 108

Instructions
13. Battleships 109
14. Making an aquarium 110
15. How to find information in a book 112

Report
16. The Ashton Cricket Club 114
17. The Garden Produce Show 116

Explanation
18. The water cycle 118
19. Ice-caps 119
20. Canal locks 120

Argument
21. Homework 122

Answers to supplementary units 123

The publishers would like to thank the following for permission to reproduce copyright material.

(page 42) Harper & Row for the extract from *Julie of the Wolves* by Jean Craighead George, Harper & Row, 1972.

(pages 92, 98, 95, 100) Dave Higham Associates for the use of the extract 'Cinderella' from *Revolting Rhymes* by Roald Dahl © Roald Dahl 1984 (1984, Puffin) and 'Dreams' from *The BFG* by Roald Dahl © Roald Dahl 1984 (1984, Penguin); 'The Story of Giant Kippernose' from *John Cunliffe's Giant Stories* © John Cunliffe 1994 (1994, Andrè Deutsch); 'The cave' from *Stig of the Dump* by Clive King © Clive King 1970 (1970, Puffin).

(page 120) Thomas Nelson & Sons Ltd for the second and third paragraphs in 'Canal locks' from *Targets* 4 by Dorothy Brogden © Dorothy Brogden 1983 (1983, Thomas Nelson & Sons Ltd).

(page 96) Penguin Putnam Inc. (USA) for the use of an extract from *Cam Jansen and the Mystery of the* UFO by David A Adler © David A Adler 1980 (1980, Viking Penguin, a division of Penguin Putnam Inc.).

(pages 91, 94) Peters Fraser and Dunlop for 'Thirty-two lengths' by Michael Rosen from *Quick, Let's Get Out Of Here* © Michael Rosen 1985 (1985, Puffin); 'Grammar' by Michael Rosen from *Excuses, Excuses* compiled by John Foster © Michael Rosen 1997 (1997, Oxford University Press).

(page 106) Stanley Thornes Ltd for the use of 'The Beatles' from *People in British History* by Tony T Triggs (1985, Basil Blackwell).

(page 102) A P Watt Ltd on behalf of Dick King-Smith for the use of an extract from *Harry's Mad* by Dick King-Smith © Dick King-Smith 1986 (1986, Puffin).

(pages 24, 28) 'Too early' and 'Me-moving' by Gordon Winch from *Mulga Bill Rides Again*, compiled by Gordon Winch, Macmillan of Australia, Melbourne, 1988.

(page 22) 'Door' by Valerie Worth © Valerie Worth 1977 by permission of the Estate of the late Valerie Worth.

Every effort has been made to trace copyright holders for the works reproduced in this book and the publishers apologise for any inadvertent omissions.

Introduction

Comprehension means 'understanding' and, in its narrowest sense, comprehension material tests children's understanding of what they read. However, true 'comprehension' goes much deeper than this. Therefore the main objective of the *Scholastic Literacy Skills: Comprehension* series is to foster reading and comprehension skills in the widest possible sense, so that children not only learn how to read, and to extract information from a variety of types of text, but also begin to appreciate the enjoyment and learning they can gain from a range of books. While the children are working on activities in this series, they will become more aware of the different features of various types of text genres, and will begin to understand how organisation of language, choice of vocabulary, grammar, layout and presentation all influence meaning.

The complete series consists of five photocopiable skills activity books, one for Key Stage 1/P1–3 (ages 5–7) and one for each of the years of Key Stage 2/P4–7 (ages 7–8; ages 8–9; ages 9–10; and ages 10–11).

Working at text level

This series of comprehension books gives children opportunities to work at text level. It is well known that text-level work gives an essential context for work at sentence and word levels. It is also an essential part of the meaning-making process, which is at the heart of effective reading.

Typical activities in text-level work are identifying main points, awareness of organisation and linguistic features of different text genres, differentiating fact, opinion and persuasion, and awareness of tense, mood and person in writing and how they affect meaning. You will find all these aspects of comprehension, and more, represented in the *Scholastic Literacy Skills: Comprehension* series.

Reading strategies

In order to learn to read well, a reader must be motivated. The variety of reading material offered by this series will ensure that children's interest will be captured so that their reading confidence will be developed.

Testing comprehension can never be a precise art. Any reader brings to new text a considerable 'baggage' of opinions, knowledge (or lack of it) and personal experience. All of these factors are bound to affect how that person responds to what they are reading and how much, or what type of, information they will retrieve from it.

To be able to understand a text fully, the reader will need to have acquired the skills of detailed (close) reading, and search reading (including skimming and scanning). To answer questions on the content of the text, the reader will require retrieval skills to locate and select the appropriate information, as well as communication skills to express responses verbally or in writing.

Close reading

Reading a text in detail gives the reader a clear understanding of what it contains. The passage should usually be read more than once, particularly if its content or subject matter is difficult or unfamiliar. This initial read through should allow the reader to fully grasp the meaning and intent of the author.

Skimming and scanning

Once the reader is familiar with the text and understands it, search skills are required if the information needed to respond to a particular question is to be located swiftly. The reader needs to be able to skim through the passage quickly and scan the parts of the text where the answer might lie.

Answering the questions

Answering comprehension questions can be challenging for a young reader, particularly in the early stages. It would be of value to the children if the texts, and possible answers to the questions, could be discussed in small groups before they are asked to work individually. This will help them to structure their answers and will also support any children who have limited reading and writing skills. Children should always be encouraged to answer the questions in complete sentences, where appropriate, as this will also enhance their writing skills.

Types of question

The four aspects of comprehension covered by questions in this book are literal, inferential, deductive and evaluative comprehension. Each of these tests a different facet of the reader's understanding of the texts. Explanations of these four types are given below, but it should be recognised that there is a considerable amount of overlap and that questions may sometimes fall between two or more categories.

• **Literal comprehension** centres on ideas and information that are quite explicit in a particular text. The reader is required to locate the response to a question, the clues to which lie on the surface of the text. In its simplest form, literal comprehension can be the recognition or recall of a single fact or incident, but it can also take more complex forms, such as the recognition or recall of a series of facts or the sequencing of incidents.

- **Inferential comprehension** requires the reader to 'read between the lines'. The information needed to respond to an inferential question is implicit in the text, and the reader needs to make inferences based on what has been read to formulate an answer. This type of question is more challenging, as it explores the extent to which the reader is aware of the nuances of meaning in the text. Children may, initially, need help to look for hidden clues and to link cause and effect.

- **Deductive comprehension** demands that the reader delves even deeper into the passage to make inferences based, not only on the text, but also on the reader's own experience and background knowledge. The reader is required to draw on personal knowledge and demonstrate a broader understanding of the text using links of cause and effect drawn from experience. Again, children may need support and guidance in formulating their answers.

- **Evaluative comprehension** asks the reader to make an evaluation of arguments or ideas suggested by the text. In order to do this, readers need to compare the information provided with their own experiences, knowledge or values. Answers given to this type of question depend on readers' assessment of a situation and how they would react to it, given their own inclinations and experiences. Generally, it is not possible to provide set answers to these questions, although pointers to the areas that should be covered are sometimes offered.

Using this book

The activities in this book unite the skills of reading and writing. They also involve speaking and listening as the work is discussed with the children before they make a written response. Each of the main and supplementary units comprise a reading comprehension passage followed by questions that focus on the four types of comprehension described above. The passages cover a variety and balance of eight different fiction and non-fiction genres and the activities are arranged in groups by genre. (The genre of each passage is indicated on each page.) The eight text genres are:

Fiction
- poetry
- drama
- narrative

Non-fiction
- recount
- instructions
- report
- explanation
- argument

The main units

Each of the 30 main units in this book follows the same pattern. It begins with an introductory section, which gives some brief information on the purpose or structure of the relevant genre. This is followed by a 'Before you read' section, which offers one or two questions to engage the reader's attention and raise awareness of the content of the unit. These questions could form the basis of a small group discussion before the reading task is attempted.

The introductory sections are followed by a reading passage. These passages gradually increase in length and difficulty throughout the series to extend children's reading experience and foster reading development. The reading passage is followed by about ten comprehension questions based on the text. The questions are designed to test the four main types of reading comprehension already discussed.

In the early stages, the emphasis is on literal comprehension, and appropriate answers to the questions could be discussed in small groups. The children should then be encouraged to answer the questions in their own words, using full sentences. This approach would be particularly helpful to children who need guidance in locating the specific relevant information and making the appropriate inferences from the text. Children will respond in different ways to the evaluative questions, as answers depend on their

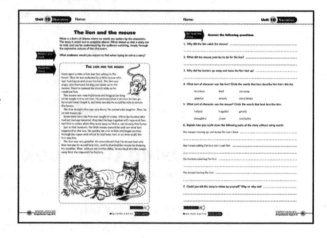

own experiences and preferences. For these too, discussion would help them to formulate responses. As children gain experience and confidence, they will become more able to work through the units on their own, with the minimum of adult help.

The final section of each unit offers suggestions for further activities, loosely related to the content of the unit, which more able children might wish to try.

Suggested answers to the questions in the main units can be found on pages 82–90 of this book.

The supplementary units

The supplementary units in this book complement and reinforce the work of the main units. They contain further examples of the genres represented in the main units – poetry, narrative, drama, recount, instructions, report, explanation and argument – thus offering the children a wider variety of fiction and non-fiction texts. As with the main units, the

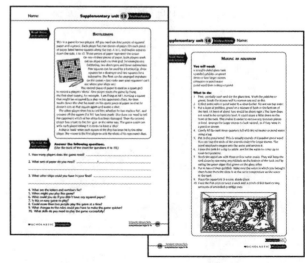

supplementary units are grouped by genre and are designed to match the target age group. Within each genre group, the passages increase in length and number of questions to offer a progression. The questions posed are balanced to give equal weight to the four types of comprehension already discussed.

Children working on one of the supplementary units should first read the passage, preferably in a small group. They should then be given the opportunity to discuss the passage and possible answers to the comprehension questions. Next, the children should answer the questions, trying always to use their own words rather than repeating sections of the text. It is important that they develop the habit of reorganising and rephrasing the information they take from a text. The ability to do this will demonstrate their understanding of what they have read. As always, questions should be answered in complete sentences where appropriate, rather than with one word or a phrase.

Suggested answers to the questions in the supplementary units can be found on pages 123–8 of this book.

The answers

All answers are laid out clearly, unit by unit. At the start of each section, a listing of question types for the passage is given, which identifies how many questions there are in each category – literal, inferential, evaluative and deductive.

Answers are given as directly as possible. Where children are likely to give a range of replies, this is introduced by the phrase 'Answers may vary', followed by suggestions of the types of points answers should cover. Where questions depend almost entirely on the individual's experience and opinions, the phrase 'Own answer' is given. Obviously situations may arise where children's answers may differ greatly from those suggested. It is usually worth checking the child's understanding and method of expression while also rejecting (though kindly) inventive or purely hopeful answers.

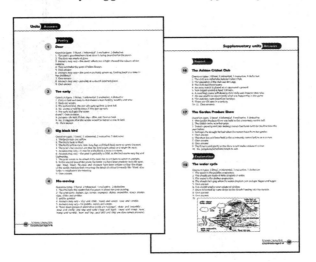

Poetry genre

DOOR

compresses ideas
– uses less 'space'
than prose

plays with
sounds of words
and rhythms of
phrases

uses word pictures
to build sensory
impressions and
create images

My grandmother's
Glass front door
Held a fancy pattern
Of panes, their
Heavy edges cut
On a slant; when
Sun shone through
They scattered
Some eighty little
Flakes of rainbows
Into the room,
Walking the walls,
Glowing like fallen
Flowers on the floor;
Why don't they
Make front doors that
Way any more?

Valerie Worth

Narrative genre

ANDROCLES AND THE LION

involves characters, setting and plot that work together to open the action

A slave named Androcles fled from his master and hid in the forest. There he came upon a lion, lying on the ground moaning and groaning.

Androcles ran away in fear, but when the lion did not follow him he turned back to find out what was wrong. The lion was obviously in great pain, and held out a swollen and bleeding paw in which Androcles could see a huge thorn.

Androcles was filled with pity. He pulled out the thorn and bandaged the bleeding paw. The lion got up and licked the hand of Androcles as a dog might do. It wanted to show that it understood, and was grateful for his help.

presents a problem to solve

Soon afterwards, Androcles was captured by soldiers out hunting for wild animals to be used in the arena. For his punishment, Androcles was to be thrown to a lion to be eaten. The Emperor and all his court came to watch the event.

Androcles was left in the middle of the arena and the lion was let loose. It had been without food for three days and rushed towards its victim. But suddenly, just before it sprang to kill, it stopped. Instead of eating Androcles, it came up and licked his hand like a dog.

Androcles could not believe his luck! This was the same lion that he had helped in the forest. It had recognised its friend just in time.

ends the narrative with a solution to the problem

The Emperor was amazed at what had happened, and asked Androcles to tell him the whole story. It moved him so much that he freed Androcles from slavery. The lion was also freed, and was allowed to return to the forest to live out the rest of its life in safety.

Drama genre

THE HARE WITH MANY FRIENDS

tells a story via the setting, sound effects and dialogue between characters

A Hare is running away from a pack of hounds, who are heard throughout the play baying and barking in the background. The noise of the hounds gets louder as the play proceeds.

NARRATOR: Hare had always thought he was popular with the other animals. Then one sunny day, he heard a pack of hounds. He realised that they were coming his way and so rushed off to seek help from his friends. The first friend he met was Bull.

HARE: I'm so glad I've found you, Bull. Those hounds are after me. I want you to charge at them and frighten them with your horns.

layout and punctuations conventions

BULL: I'm very sorry, Hare, I have to meet someone. But I feel sure that our friend Goat will do what you want.

NARRATOR: Hare ran off to find Goat, who was eating some flowers.

HARE: Quick, my good friend Goat. The hounds are after me and I need your help. I want you to butt those awful hounds when they reach here. I'll just jump up on your back to be out of the way.

speaker's name; colon

GOAT: No, don't do that, Hare. I don't think I can help. I've had a bad back and I don't think it would be helped if you jumped up there.

NARRATOR: Hare, by this time, was getting very worried that none of his friends really seemed to want to help, but he knew Ram wouldn't let him down. He found him grazing in a field near the stream.

HARE: Ram, I need your help and I need it now. Can you hear the pack of hounds that is after me?

involves what the characters actually say

RAM: Oh Hare, I really feel I can't. Hounds, you know, are just as likely to eat sheep as hares.

NARRATOR: Finally, Hare went off to find Calf. He realised that this friend was his last hope.

HARE: Calf, please, please can you help me? Nobody else is able to and I don't know where else to turn.

CALF: I'd like to, Hare. But if the others, who are so much bigger and stronger, can't help, how can I be of any use? Ask someone else.

is usually in present tense

(The Hare darts backwards and forwards to the sound of the hounds coming closer.)

NARRATOR: The hounds were now very close. Hare ran as fast as he could into the deepest part of the forest, where he found a safe place to hide. *(The sound of the hounds gradually dies away. The Hare drops down exhausted.)* Luckily, the hounds missed him, but as he lay there panting, he murmured, "So much for friends."

Recount genre

is in past tense

deals in facts

uses action verbs

may be personal (involves 'I' or 'we')

contains details

is usually chronological

OUR TRIP TO SHINGLE COVE

During the summer holidays we went on a trip to Shingle Cove, a small town near the sea. Mum, Dad and I went, and my friend Jody. We stayed in a cottage for a week.

Every morning we walked to the beach for a swim. On some days the water was rough, but on other days it was calm. Jody and I used to race down the beach and jump into the sea!

Some afternoons, Dad, Jody and I played golf at a course near the end of the beach. Dad can hit the ball a really long way. Jody and I only ever managed to beat him on one hole, and it was short.

While we were away, Mum spent the afternoons reading her book. She said she enjoyed the peace!

One day Jody and I found a secret path to the beach. We had to scramble through some gorse and down a rocky track. It was a bit scary at times and we had to be careful. We got to the beach long before Mum and Dad. They went along the road and took ages.

In the evenings we sometimes had a barbecue, then afterwards we would sit on the patio and look out over the sea. If the weather wasn't warm we would play cards on the table inside. Jody and I never wanted to go to bed.

We were all very sad when we had to go home. I really liked Shingle Cove. I hope we can go back there again next year.

may involve a narrative structure, for example autobiography

may involve personal feelings and opinions

Instructions genre

describes how to
carry out a process
or procedure

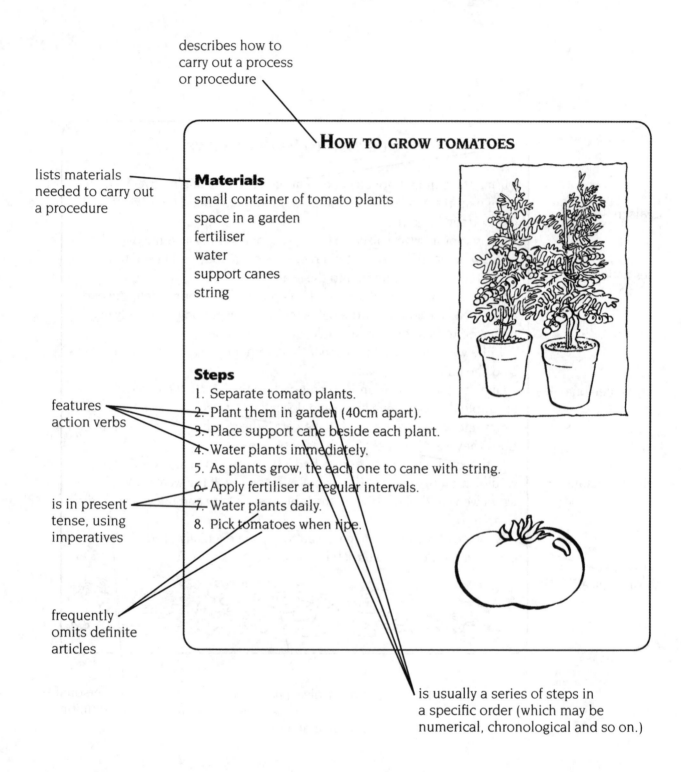

How to grow tomatoes

Materials
small container of tomato plants
space in a garden
fertiliser
water
support canes
string

lists materials
needed to carry out
a procedure

Steps
1. Separate tomato plants.
2. Plant them in garden (40cm apart).
3. Place support cane beside each plant.
4. Water plants immediately.
5. As plants grow, tie each one to cane with string.
6. Apply fertiliser at regular intervals.
7. Water plants daily.
8. Pick tomatoes when ripe.

features
action verbs

is in present
tense, using
imperatives

frequently
omits definite
articles

is usually a series of steps in
a specific order (which may be
numerical, chronological and so on.)

Report genre

focuses on a specific subject or idea

is usually in present tense

provides facts and examples to support the subject

THE ELEPHANT

Elephants are the largest land animals in the world. They live in Africa and the south of Asia.

There are two kinds of elephant – African and Indian. African elephants are bigger than Indian elephants. They often weigh five or six tonnes, and can be even more! It is easy to tell the difference between the two types. African elephants have sloping foreheads and very large ears. They are also darker in colour.

Elephants eat plants, fruit and the young shoots of trees, using their amazing noses, or trunks, to put food into their mouths. They also use their trunks for drinking. Water is sucked up by the trunk and is then squirted into the mouth. Elephants drink a lot of water, often more than 100 litres in a day.

Elephants use their trunks to lift things. They are very strong and can pull and carry big loads. They often live for about 50 years, a long life for an animal.

Sad to say, these wonderful animals are under threat in the wild. They are hunted for their tusks, which are made of ivory and are therefore very valuable.

However, plastics and other materials can now often be used instead of ivory, and wild elephants are protected in many parts of the world. It is hoped that, in time, their numbers will increase.

Explanation genre

describes how something works
or why something happens

How we digest our food

General statement
The food we eat has to be changed into
many things, including muscles, bones,
blood and energy. This process is called
digestion.

involves facts

Points that explain
First, the food is chewed and mixed with
saliva in the mouth. Then it is swallowed
and goes into the stomach.
In the stomach, the food is mixed with
gastric juices. It is then sent to the small
intestine where it is mixed again with bile
from the liver. This helps to digest the fats.
Digestive juices from the pancreas break
down the starch and sugar.
As the pulp (the digesting food) moves
along the small intestine, the nutrients
(the important building blocks of the body)
are absorbed into the bloodstream. What
is left is passed into the large intestine and
finally out of the body.

is usually in
present tense,

using a series of
steps in a
specific order

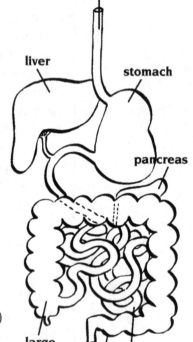

from mouth

liver

stomach

pancreas

large
intestine

small
intestine

may involve diagrams

Argument genre

has an opening
statement

puts forward a point of view

A VARIED DIET IS BEST

Humans need to eat different kinds of foods if they are to have a balanced
diet. If they do this, they will grow fit and strong, have plenty of energy
and enjoy good health.

Some foods provide us with proteins which make the body grow. Some
foods are rich in carbohydrates or fats; these give us energy. Other foods
are rich in vitamins and minerals; they help to keep us fit and well.

No one food can supply all the things we need. That is why it is
important to eat a wide range of foods.

We need to eat foods like meat, fish, nuts, eggs and cheese for proteins;
we should include grains, sugar and fats to give us energy; it is also
important to eat fruit and vegetables for minerals and vitamins.

If we include these foods, and others, in our meals then we can be sure
that we are eating a varied and balanced diet.

a series of reasons
or evidence for the
argument which
may involve
details and facts

a closing
statement which
sums up the
argument; usually
in present tense

Assessment

Scholastic Literacy Skills: Comprehension can be valuable in helping you to assess a child's developing progress in English. Comprehension exercises test, above all, children's ability to read and make sense of text. Because the reading passages are appropriately labelled with a particular genre name, it is relatively easy to spot whether a child is less or more able to tackle and make sense of specific types of text. Moreover, by looking at whether particular questions are inferential, deductive, evaluative or literal, it is also easy to recognise areas where the child is having difficulty. In either case, there is a wide range of differentiated material to choose from in the main and supplementary units in this book, which will challenge or build confidence in most children in the primary school.

Photocopiables for assessment and record-keeping

Pupil's record and evaluation sheet
This has been designed to be completed mainly by the children. It provides a record of the units covered by each child and allows each child to indicate his or her interest, level of difficulty and level of achievement. It is useful in highlighting individual patterns of needs, interests and strengths. It also builds a strong sense of achievement in each child.

Class record of progress
This follows the class as it moves through the school, providing a record of what has been covered in each year. It can help teachers find a starting point with a new class. It also helps with progression between year groups.

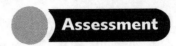

Pupil's record and evaluation sheet

[Name] _____ 's record

Fill in the chart for each unit you complete.
Use these symbols, or make up your own.

Date	Unit	Did I enjoy it?	Was my work good?	Was it easy?

Teacher's comments

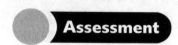
Class record of achievement

Unit	Title	Genre	Date
1	Door	Poetry	
2	Too early	Poetry	
3	Big black bird	Poetry	
4	Me-moving	Poetry	
5	Thesues slays the Mintoaur	Narrative	
6	Lauren and the flying dog (1)	Narrative	
7	Lauren and the flying dog (2)	Narrative	
8	Androcles and the lion	Narrative	
9	The amazing Tamara Mudpuddle	Narrative	
10	The lion and the mouse	Narrative	
11	Julie of the Wolves	Narrative	
12	Tom	Narrative	
13	The Hare with many friends	Drama	
14	The storm	Drama	
15	Brer Rabbit and the tar baby	Drama	
16	Our trip to Shingle Cove	Recount	
17	Flat Stanley	Recount	
18	How to catch a train	Instructions	
19	How to grow tomatoes	Instructions	
20	Catching a fish	Instructions	
21	Sports day	Report	
22	The elephant	Report	
23	The earthworm	Report	
24	How a rainbow is made	Explanation	
25	How we digest our food	Explanation	
26	Why an iceberg floats	Explanation	
27	Why some spiders have webs	Explanation	
28	A varied diet is best	Argument	
29	Team games are more fun	Argument	
30	Cats make good pets	Argument	

Class record of achievement

Supplementary unit	Title	Genre	Date
1	Thirty-two lengths	Poetry	
2	Cinderella	Poetry	
3	Grammar	Poetry	
4	A centipede	Poetry	
5	Cam Jansen and the mystery of the UFO	Narrative	
6	Dreams	Narrative	
7	The cave	Narrative	
8	Harry's Mad	Narrative	
9	The strange creature	Drama	
10	The rescue	Drama	
11	The Beatles	Recount	
12	Swimming lessons	Recount	
13	Battleships	Instructions	
14	Making an aquarium	Instructions	
15	How to find information in a book	Instructions	
16	The Ashton Cricket Club	Report	
17	The Garden Produce Show	Report	
18	The water cycle	Explanation	
19	Ice-caps	Explanation	
20	Canal locks	Explanation	
21	Homework	Argument	

Door

This poem is about a front door that the poet remembers from her childhood. It has an unusual, uneven rhythm and the ends of the lines do not rhyme.

Before you read

- What is your front door like?
- Sometimes, when it rains, you can see a rainbow. What colours might you see?

Read this poem

DOOR

My grandmother's
Glass front door
Held a fancy pattern
Of panes, their
Heavy edges cut
On a slant; when
Sun shone through
They scattered
Some eighty little
Flakes of rainbows
Into the room,
Walking the walls,
Glowing like fallen
Flowers on the floor;
Why don't they
Make front doors that
Way any more?

Valerie Worth

Re-read the poem

Answer the following questions.

1. Whose door is being described in the poem? _____

2. What was the door made of? _____

3. As light came through the panes of glass, it looked like **flakes of rainbows**. What do you think the author means?

_____

_____

_____

Continued on ▶P23

4. What did the **flakes of rainbows** remind the poet of? _____

_____

_____

5. Why do you think the poet liked her grandmother's front door? _____

_____

_____

6. Do you think the poet is grown up now, or still a child? Why? _____

_____

_____

7. The poet doesn't seem to like modern front doors. Explain why you think she feels that way.

_____

_____

_____

8. Where else might you see sunshine through coloured glass windows? _____

_____

_____

9. Do you like the look of sunshine streaming though coloured windows? Give reasons for your answer.

_____

_____

_____

More things to do

- Can you remember something special about when you were younger? Try to write a poem about it.
- Draw a diagram showing how light is broken up into parts as it passes through a glass prism. Label your diagram.

Continued from P22

Too early

The first verse of this poem is a well-known proverb, a wise, old saying which you will probably have heard before. The rest of the poem gives a twist to the proverb, especially the last verse.

Before you read ➤

Here are the beginnings of some sayings. Try and complete them, then discuss what each one might mean and whether you agree with the saying.

A stitch in time _____ _____ .

Children should be seen and _____ _____ .

Great oaks from little acorns _____ .

All that glitters is _____ _____ .

Read this poem ➤

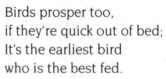

TOO EARLY

Early to bed
and early to rise
makes a man healthy,
wealthy and wise.

Birds prosper too,
if they're quick out of bed;
It's the earliest bird
who is the best fed.

But think of the worms
on which birds dine and sup.
They'd be much better off
if they didn't get up.

Gordon Winch

Continued on ▶ P25

■SCHOLASTIC **Photocopiable**

Re-read the poem ➤ **Answer the following questions.**

1. What is the well-known proverb expressed in the poem? _____

_____

2. What do birds eat? _____

3. Which bird is best fed? _____

4. Would worms also eat well if they got up early? _____

_____

5. What saying or proverb is the second verse based on? _____

_____

6. Why would getting out of bed early make a person healthy, wealthy and wise? _____

_____

_____

7. Do you like getting up early? Why? _____

_____

_____

8. Explain the meaning of:

prosper _____

sup _____

9. Does the last verse agree with what the proverb says? In what way? _____

_____

_____

10. Complete this verse:

Late to bed
and late to rise
makes a _____, _____ _____ and _____.

Remember that poems do not have to rhyme!

Continued from P24 ➤

SCHOLASTIC **Photocopiable**

Big black bird

Sometimes the shape of a poem is important. The way in which a poem is laid out on the page (and the style and size of the lettering) can make it more interesting.

Before you read

Look at this shape poem, which has been written in the shape of the subject of the poem (the thing being written about).

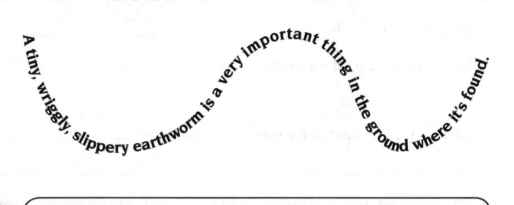

A tiny, wriggly, slippery earthworm is a very important thing in the ground where it's found.

Read this poem

BIG BLACK BIRD

There's a bird in our garden
With big yellow

I'd go right up to him
Except for his **size**

His legs are so **l o n g**

And his beak is so **BLACK**

That if I came near him,
I know he'd attack.

And if I got too close
He could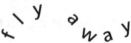

So I'll watch from a

And then he will stay –
And I'll go near… one day.

Gordon Winch

Re-read the poem

Answer the following questions.

1. What colour are the bird's eyes? _____

2. What colour is the bird's beak? _____

Continued on P27

SCHOLASTIC Photocopiable

3. What things about the bird seem to worry the poet? _____

_____

_____

4. What are the two excuses the poet makes for not coming closer? _____

_____

_____

5. What type of bird do you think this might be? _____

_____

6. Do you think the poet is an adult or a child? _____

_____

7. Poems often tell us a great deal about the feelings of the writer. What does this poem tell you about the poet's feelings?

_____

_____

_____

8. What special uses of size, shape or colour have been made in this poem? _____

_____

_____

_____

_____

9. What would you do if you met a big black bird in the garden? _____

_____

_____

_____

More things to do

- Read this poem aloud to your group with expression. Try to show how the poet was feeling.
- Write your own shape poem about a subject of your choice.

Continued from P26

SCHOLASTIC **Photocopiable**

Me-moving

Poems are often full of action and movement. This poem is full of action of a special kind: it describes many of the ways in which you can move.

Before you read

Think back to your last holiday. Were there any things you did that involved moving in a special way, such as swimming or riding?

Read this poem

ME-MOVING

I dart and dash,
I jig and jump,
I scamper, skate and scramble.
I strut and stride,
I slip and slide,
And frequently, I amble.

I leap and lurch,
I crawl and creep,
I rove and romp and ramble.
I turn and trip,
I skid and skip,
And now and then –
I gambol!

Gordon Winch

Re-read the poem

Answer the following questions.

1. What does the title say that the poem is about? _____

_____

2. List the different types of movement the poet does in the first verse. _____

_____

_____

3. What does the poet do:

frequently _____

now and then? _____

Continued on P29

SCHOLASTIC Photocopiable

4. **Dart** and **dash** are words of similar meaning. Find three more pairs of words with similar meanings in this poem.

_____

_____

_____

5. Does the poet ever move slowly? _____

6. Many words in this poem are alliterative. That means that they start with the some sound or sounds. **Dart** and **dash**; **jig** and **jump** are two sets of alliterative words. Write down three more pairs or groups of alliterative words.

_____

_____

_____

7. What type of movement in this poem could you not do on your feet? _____

_____

8. Poems can tell a story, describe a person's feelings, make a comment on the writer's beliefs and many other things. Write what you think this poem does.

_____

_____

9. What do these words mean? Use a dictionary to help you.

amble _____

gambol _____

10. Which movements in this poem would you most enjoy doing? Choose as many as you like.

_____

_____

_____

More things to do

Write your own action poem using verbs which describe what you do at home. Give your poem the title 'Me – at home'. The verbs you use may need to imply less movement, such as **read** and **sit**.

Continued from P28

Theseus slays the Minotaur

A myth is an old story (a narrative) which tells of magical happenings long ago. It usually involves gods, heroes and other imaginary men and women or creatures. This myth, like many others, comes from Ancient Greece.

Before you read

You may have heard or read other Greek myths. Can you finish any of these sentences?

Hercules was very _____ .

Pegasus was a winged _____ .

Midas had a _____ touch.

The Cyclops had only one _____ .

Read this myth

THESEUS SLAYS THE MINOTAUR

The Minotaur was a terrible creature, half man and half bull. It lived under the palace of King Minos at Knossus in Crete. Its home was a labyrinth, a maze of passageways. No one could find the way in or out.

When the Minotaur was hungry it would bellow so loudly that the whole palace would shake. When this happened a human sacrifice had to be made to the monster, as it ate only human flesh. In its lair were piles of bones of young men and women who had been its victims.

The people of nearby Athens had been forced to send many of their sons and daughters to feed the Minotaur. King Minos was very powerful, and the Athenians had no choice but to obey his commands.

Theseus, the son of King Aegeus of Athens, was a very brave young man. He vowed he would slay the Minotaur. Old Aegeus begged him not to take the risk, but Theseus was determined to kill the monster. So, when the next victims set sail for Crete, Theseus went with them.

King Minos had a beautiful daughter named Ariadne. When she saw the handsome and brave Theseus, she immediately fell deeply in love and decided to help him kill the dreaded Minotaur.

Under cover of night she went to visit Theseus, who was in prison with the other victims.

"Take this ball of thread," she said. "Tie one end of it to the gate of the labyrinth before you go in, so you can follow it and find your way out again. If you go now you will be able to kill the Minotaur while it is sleeping. I will wait for you at the gate."

Theseus did what Ariadne had told him to do. He walked through the maze of passageways until he reached the sleeping Minotaur. Without wasting a second, he leapt upon the monster and slew it with his bare hands. Then he followed the thread back to the gate.

Ariadne and Theseus freed the other prisoners and together they made their escape from the island of Crete. All the people in Athens rejoiced that the Minotaur was dead.

Continued on P31

Re-read the myth ➤ **Answer the following questions.**

1. ● What was the Minotaur? _____

_____

   ● What did it eat? _____

_____

   ● Where did it live? _____

2. Who was Theseus? How did he find his way out of the labyrinth? _____

_____

_____

3. Do you know where Athens and Crete are? Find them on a map.

4. How do you know that Theseus was brave? _____

_____

5. What did Theseus do which showed that he was very strong? _____

_____

6. Why do you think that the people of Athens rejoiced that the Minotaur was dead? _____

_____

_____

7. Ariadne deceived her father when she helped Theseus. Do you think she did the right thing? Why?

_____

_____

_____

More things to do ➤
● Read some more Greek myths.
● Draw a picture of the Minotaur, imagining what it looked like.

Continued from P30 ➤

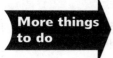

SCHOLASTIC Photocopiable

Lauren and the flying dog (1)

A narrative is a story that begins by telling the reader where and when things are happening. This introduction is called the orientation. The story continues with a series of events, one of which causes a change in the plot. This change is called a complication. The story ends when the events are worked out. This is called the resolution. This fantasy story is in two parts.

Before you read

- If you had a large dog who could fly you anywhere, where would you go?
- If you were flying on the back of a dog, what difficulties might you have?

Read this story

LAUREN AND THE FLYING DOG

It was a horrible night. A strong wind was howling around the house. Lauren was afraid that there was going to be a storm with lots of thunder and lightning. She had wanted her dog, Sheeba, to stay inside tonight, but Mum had said that she must sleep in the garage as usual. Lauren felt sure that Sheeba had wanted to stay with her.

When Lauren went to bed she listened to the wind howling and the rain pelting down. She felt warm and snug but she was worried about Sheeba. Suddenly she heard a strange noise behind her head. It sounded like someone scratching on the window pane.

"Come on Lauren," she heard a voice call. "Get up and let me in."

"Who is it?" she asked.

"It's me, Sheeba."

Lauren was amazed. She stood up on the bed and reached over to pull back the curtains. There, just in front of the window, floated Sheeba. Lauren opened the window and Sheeba drifted inside.

"I thought I'd show you how dogs really live," said Sheeba. "Come on. There's no need to get dressed."

Lauren jumped on to Sheeba's back and together they shot out through the window. Suddenly the rain and the wind seemed to have disappeared. It was no longer night and they were flying through bright sunlight.

"Where are we going, Sheeba?" asked Lauren.

"We're going north to visit my friends, Beth and Angus."

Lauren couldn't believe how quickly they were travelling, and soon they began to descend towards the ground. Lauren could see a group of dogs dancing to the music of bagpipes. As they landed, Beth the Border Collie called out to them. "Hi there, Sheeba. Who's your friend? Come and join in the Games."

Angus the Airedale raced over to greet them. When he saw that Lauren was wearing her nightclothes he said, "You'll catch your death in those. You need a kilt, my girl." With that, he rushed off to get one.

The music was still playing when Angus brought the kilt. Lauren put it on over her pyjamas. Then they all did 'The Dashing White Sergeant'.

Continued on P33

SCHOLASTIC **Photocopiable**

Re-read the story → **Answer the following questions.**

1. Why didn't Lauren want Sheeba to sleep out in the garage? _____

_____

2. Who insisted that Sheeba go out into the garage? _____

_____

3. Where was Lauren when she heard a voice calling her? _____

_____

4. What happened when Lauren got on to Sheeba's back? _____

_____

5. Where do you think Beth the Border Collie and Angus the Airedale live? _____

_____

6. Do you think Lauren would have been a bit frightened when she heard the voice calling? Why?

_____

_____

7. Can you think of two reasons why Lauren might have been feeling cold? _____

_____

_____

8. What sorts of things happen at a Highland Games? _____

_____

_____

9. What is 'The Dashing White Sergeant'? _____

_____

More things to do → Before reading the next part of the story, make up your own ending and tell it to a friend. You might even choose to take Lauren and Sheeba on another adventure. Later you will be able to compare it to the one in the second part of this story.

Continued from P32 →

SCHOLASTIC **Photocopiable**

Lauren and the flying dog (2)

A narrative is a story that opens with a description of where and when things are happening. This introduction is called the orientation. The story continues with a series of events, one of which causes a change in the story. This is called a complication. The story ends when the events are worked out. This is called the resolution and is the concluding part of the story.

Before you read

- Re-read part 1 of this story on pages 32 to 33.
- Think about the ending you made up for this story. Check to see if your friend can remember the ending you made up.

Read this story

LAUREN AND THE FLYING DOG

Lauren had never had so much fun in all her life. Sheeba's friends were so kind to her, and the dancing was wonderful.

"We'd better be going," puffed Sheeba. "I want you to meet Fifi and Pierre. They're French poodles and own a famous café, in Paris. It's just a short hop across the water."

Everyone waved to them as they rose into the air. In a second they were flying over Paris, then with a gentle bump landed outside a café, called L'Ironique. Sheeba led the way through the doors.

"Ma *cherie*, Sheeba," called Fifi. "It is lovely to see you and your friend. 'Ere is Pierre. 'E will be so pleased that you are here again."

Pierre put down his tray and rushed over to kiss Sheeba on both cheeks. Then he did the same to Lauren.

"Welcome to Paris," he said, "ze most *belle* city in all ze world. You will have coffee and croissants, no?"

Just as the food and drink arrived some music started. Everyone began to clap loudly in time to the music. Dancers in beautiful costumes ran out on to the stage. They kicked their legs up high, flapping the sides of their frilly skirts.

"Ze famous cancan," shouted Pierre.

Lauren thought it was so exciting. She jumped up on the stage and started to dance. She flapped the sides of her kilt and kicked her legs as high as she could. She turned and twirled with the other dancers, and finally she jumped high into the air and came down on the floor, doing the splits.

All the people in the café, leapt to their feet and applauded.

"You were *magnifique*," said Pierre. "You 'av a real future as a dancer. You must stay in Paris and live with us. We will send you to ballet school. You will be very famous one day, very famous…"

Suddenly Lauren was awake and back in her room. It was morning and the sun was shining in through the open window. But why was the window open? Lauren was sure that her mother had closed it tight last night. Probably the wind and rain did that… Or was it…? She heard Sheeba barking at the milkman.

Continued on P35

■ SCHOLASTIC   Photocopiable

Re-read the story ➤   **Answer the following questions.**

1. Who was Lauren going to meet in Paris? _____

_____

2. What is the name of the café, owned by Fifi and Pierre? _____

_____

3. What was the name of the dance Lauren joined in with? _____

4. What was Lauren wearing when she got to Paris? _____

_____

5. Why did Sheeba **puff** when she spoke to Lauren at the beginning? _____

_____

6. Sheeba says that Paris is **just across the water**. What do you think she is referring to?

_____

7. ● What is a croissant? _____

   ● If you were having coffee and croissants, what time of day might it be? _____

_____

8. How does the author end the story? What do you think really happened? _____

_____

_____

_____

9. Find out the meaning of the French words **cherie**, **belle** and **magnifique**.

_____

_____

_____

More things to do ➤   Think of another adventure for Sheeba and Lauren. Write out a rough outline of that adventure.

Continued from P34 ➤

Androcles and the lion

A fable is a short story that has a message, or moral, about how people should behave. The animals in fables often act like humans, and some even talk. In this story the main characters are a lion and a man who is a slave.

Before you read

- Have you heard of any of the following well-known fables? Complete the ones you know.

The Boy Who Cried _____

The Hare and the _____

The _____ and the Crow

- Do you know the moral of any of these fables?

Read this fable

ANDROCLES AND THE LION

A slave named Androcles fled from his master and hid in the forest. There he came upon a lion, lying on the ground moaning and groaning.

Androcles ran away in fear, but when the lion did not follow him he turned back to find out what was wrong. The lion was obviously in great pain, and held out a swollen and bleeding paw in which Androcles could see a huge thorn.

Androcles was filled with pity. He pulled out the thorn and bandaged the bleeding paw. The lion got up and licked the hand of Androcles as a dog might do. It wanted to show that it understood, and was grateful for his help.

Soon afterwards, Androcles was captured by soldiers out hunting for wild animals to be used in the arena. For his punishment, Androcles was to be thrown to a lion to be eaten. The Emperor and all his court came to watch the event.

Androcles was left in the middle of the arena and the lion was let loose. It had been without food for three days and rushed towards its victim. But suddenly, just before it sprang to kill, it stopped. Instead of eating Androcles, it came up and licked his hand like a dog.

Androcles could not believe his luck! This was the same lion that he had helped in the forest. It had recognised its friend just in time.

The Emperor was amazed at what had happened, and asked Androcles to tell him the whole story. It moved him so much that he freed Androcles from slavery. The lion was also freed, and was allowed to return to the forest to live out the rest of its life in safety.

Continued on P37

Re-read the fable **Answer the following questions.**

1. What did Androcles see in the forest? _____

2. Why was the animal moaning and groaning? _____

_____

3. What did Androcles do to help? _____

_____

4. When Androcles was captured and left in the middle of the arena, why didn't the lion eat him?

_____

_____

5. Is the story set in modern-day society? What clues helped you to decide this? _____

_____

_____

6. Why do you think the Emperor came to watch what was happening to Androcles in the arena?

_____

_____

7. Why was the Emperor **amazed**? _____

_____

8. What part of the story would you say was the crisis (the most tense part)? _____

_____

9. What do you think the message or moral of this fable is? _____

_____

10. Explain the meaning of:

filled with pity _____

sprang to kill _____

Continued from P36

The amazing Tamara Mudpuddle

A narrative tells a story. It has a beginning (introduction or orientation), a middle (complication or crisis) and an end (resolution). In the beginning, we meet the characters and find out when and where the story takes place. Then there are some events that happen, a crisis and an ending, in which everything is worked out.

Before you read

Name a fantasy (a story that could not really happen) that you have read, or seen on television or at the cinema.

Read this story

THE AMAZING TAMARA MUDPUDDLE

Tamara Mudpuddle rose from her chair. She rose, not to brush her teeth or go out to play. She rose much more than that: slowly, above the chair, above the table, like a hot-air balloon – until her head bumped against the ceiling of the dining room.

It happened after Tamara had eaten canned cabbage for lunch. Her grandfather had brought it back from his recent trekking tour in Tibet.

Tamara was not all that keen on cabbage, but she finished her portion. After all, it was a present, and cabbage was supposed to be good for you.

But then it had this strange effect: Tamara suddenly felt light, very light and, next thing she knew, her head bumped the ceiling.

Mr Michael Mudpuddle and his wife, Margaret, were not surprised when their daughter floated to the ceiling. She was always doing something very odd, it seemed to them.

On a visit to the zoo she had climbed to the top of the tallest tree, pretending to be a monkey, and had to be brought down by crane; she had fallen into the sea with all her clothes on while trying to fly and had to be rescued by the coastguard.

And if she wasn't doing something outrageous, she was dreaming that she was. She had been a skydiver, a jet pilot, a pop singer, a weightlifter and the captain of an ocean liner, all in one day.

"Do come down, Tamara," said her mother. "You'll dirty your clothes."

"Hmph!" said her father, and he went on reading the paper.

Continued on P39

Re-read the story ➤ **Answer the following questions.**

1. What happened after Tamara ate the canned cabbage? _____

_____

2. Where did the canned cabbage come from? _____

_____

3. Were Mr and Mrs Mudpuddle surprised when Tamara rose to the ceiling? Why? _____

_____

4. Had the Mudpuddle family had the canned cabbage for a long time? _____

_____

5. What sort of person do you think Tamara is? _____

_____

6. What sort of people do you think her parents are? _____

_____

7. What is there about this story which tells you it is a fantasy? _____

_____

_____

8. Where is Tibet, and what does **trekking** mean? _____

_____

_____

9. Would you like to eat canned cabbage? Explain why or why not. _____

_____

_____

More things to do ➤
- Write the story of how Tamara's grandfather acquired the canned cabbage. Do you think he knew it had magical qualities?
- Think of a way this story might finish. Perhaps Tamara floats out of the window; she may even go into outer space! Write the ending yourself.

Continued from P38 ➤

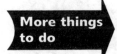

SCHOLASTIC Photocopiable

The lion and the mouse

Mime is a form of drama where no words are spoken by the characters. The story is acted out in complete silence. Mime shows us that a story can be told, and can be understood by the audience watching, simply through the expressive actions of the characters.

Before you read

What problems would you expect to find when trying to mime a story?

Read this story

THE LION AND THE MOUSE

Once upon a time a lion was fast asleep in the forest. Then he was wakened by a little mouse who was running up and down his back. The lion was angry, and thumped his big paw down on to the mouse. Then he opened his mouth wide so he could eat him.

The mouse was very frightened and begged the King of the Jungle not to eat him. He promised that if the lion let him go he would never forget it, and that one day he would be able to return the favour.

The lion thought this was very funny. He roared with laughter. Then, he let the mouse go.

Some time later, the lion was caught in a trap. When the hunters who had set the trap returned, they tied his legs together with rope and then tied him to a tree while they went away to fetch a cart to carry him home.

Just at that moment, the little mouse passed by and saw what had happened to the lion. He quickly ran over to him and began to chew through the ropes with which he had been tied. In no time at all, the lion was free.

The lion was very grateful. He remembered that the mouse had said that one day he would help him, and he thanked the mouse for keeping his promise. Then, without any further delay, he ran back into the jungle, away from the trap and the hunters.

Continued on P41

Re-read the story ➤ **Answer the following questions.**

1. Why did the lion catch the mouse? _____

_____

2. What did the mouse promise to do for the lion? _____

_____

3. Why did the hunters go away and leave the lion tied up? _____

_____

4. What sort of character was the lion? Circle the words that best describe him from this list.

ferocious	kind	uncaring
grateful	moody	considerate

5. What sort of character was the mouse? Circle the words that best describe him.

helpful	forgetful	greedy
thoughtful	clever	unreliable

6. Explain how you could show the following parts of the story without using words:

the mouse running up and down the lion's back _____

_____

the mouse asking the lion not to eat him _____

_____

the hunters catching the lion _____

_____

the mouse freeing the lion _____

_____

7. Could you tell this story in mime by yourself? Why or why not? _____

_____

_____

Continued from P40 ➤

Julie of the Wolves

An animal story is a type of narrative in which the main character is
an animal, or a human who has close contact with animals. As in any
narrative there are characters, interesting incidents which lead to a climax
(complication), and an ending (resolution) in which things are worked out.

Before you read

The passage below is from the narrative *Julie of the Wolves* by Jean
Craighead George. It is the story of Miyax, an Eskimo girl, whose English
name is Julie. She has run away from a frightening home situation and is
lost. Then she meets a pack of wolves. Can you think of one or two ways
the wolves might help her?

Read this story

JULIE OF THE WOLVES

Miyax stared hard at the regal black wolf, hoping to catch his eye. She
must somehow tell him that she was starving and ask him for food. This
could be done she knew, for her father, an Eskimo hunter, had done so.
One year he had camped near a wolf den while on a hunt. When a month
had passed and her father had seen no game, he told the leader of the
wolves that he was hungry and needed food. The next night the wolf
called him from far away and her father went to him and found a freshly
killed caribou. Unfortunately, Miyax's father never explained to her how he
had told the wolf of his needs. And not long afterwards he paddled his
kayak into the Bering Sea to hunt for seal, and he never returned.

She had been watching the wolves for two
days, trying to discern which of their sounds and
movements expressed goodwill and friendship. Most
animals had such signals. The little Arctic ground
squirrels flicked their tails sideways to notify others
of their kind that they were friendly. By imitating this
signal with her forefinger, Miyax had lured many a
squirrel to her hand. If she could discover such a
gesture for the wolves she would be able to make
friends with them and share their food, like a bird
or a fox.

Jean Craighead George

Re-read the story

Answer the following questions.

1. Why had Miyax's father become hungry when he was on a hunting trip? _____

_____

2. What had Miyax's father not explained to her? _____

_____

Continued on P43

SCHOLASTIC Photocopiable

3. What was Miyax trying to discover by watching the wolves? _____

_____

4. Why did she want to discover these things? _____

_____

5. What did the wolves have in common with other animals? _____

_____

6. How had Miyax managed to attract the Arctic ground squirrels? _____

_____

7. How do we know from this extract that travelling in the frozen north can be very dangerous?

_____

_____

8. Do you think that Miyax eventually made friendly contact with the wolves? Why? _____

_____

_____

_____

9. If you had been Miyax, how would you have felt about the situation you found yourself in?

_____

_____

_____

10. What sort of opinion do most people have of wolves? Do you think this is fair and reasonable?

_____

_____

_____

More things to do

- Write a paragraph explaining how you think Miyax (Julie) might have survived her terrible experience.
- Read the whole book, *Julie of the Wolves* by Jean Craighead George. You should be able to find it in a library.

Continued from P42

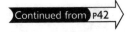 **Photocopiable**

Tom

A narrative is a story that begins by telling the reader where and when things are happening. This introduction is called the orientation. The story continues with a series of events, one of which causes the story to change. This change is called a complication. The story ends when the events are worked out. This is called the resolution.

Before you read

- What sports do you enjoy playing or watching?
- Do you think girls and boys usually enjoy the same kinds of sports?

Read this story

TOM

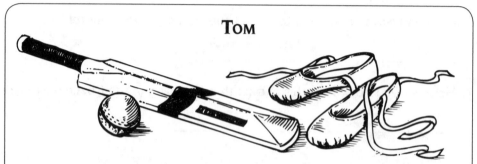

Tom is a very good cricketer. He bats very well, he opens the bowling and he hardly ever misses a ball when he is fielding. Every Saturday morning in summer he plays with his team at the local cricket pitch.

Tom's sister, Jessica, is learning ballet. The ballet school is on the way to the cricket ground, so every Saturday morning Tom and Jessica walk together to her ballet class.

One morning, when they arrived at the ballet school, Tom realised that he was very early for his match, so he asked Jessica if he could go inside and watch her class. He wasn't really very interested in ballet, but it was better than sitting by himself outside the cricket pavilion. He sat down on a chair near the door and began to watch the lesson.

"Why don't you come and join us?" asked the teacher. "All you have to do is take off your trainers."

Tom felt a bit silly with everyone looking at him, so he got up and joined the class. They started with stretches at the barre, and Tom also tried to join in when they did the splits and the *pas de chat*. He was just beginning to enjoy the class when Jessica pointed to the clock. It was time for him to leave. The rest of the class had started doing leaps, so as soon as he had finished them, he left to go and play his game.

All the way to the cricket ground he leaped and jumped around. He was last to arrive and his team were waiting for him because he was opening the batting. He felt great as he walked towards the wicket.

That day he scored a century for his team. He had never batted better. He also bowled really well, and took five wickets and two catches! Everyone picked him as the 'player of the match'.

Tom decided that the ballet class had been a terrific way to warm up for his cricket match, so now he makes sure he goes for a little while every Saturday morning.

Continued on P45

Re-read the story

Answer the following questions.
(Use the back of the sheet for question 9.)

1. When are Tom's sister's ballet classes held? _____

_____

2. What did Tom have on his feet? _____

3. Where would Tom have waited if he hadn't gone in to the ballet school? _____

_____

4. The first paragraph tells you information you need to know about Tom so that the story that follows makes sense. List the facts you learn about Tom in the first paragraph.

_____

_____

_____

5. What additional fact do you learn about Tom from the second paragraph? _____

_____

_____

6. Why do you think the ballet teacher asked Tom to join in the lesson? _____

_____

_____

7. What showed that Tom was enjoying the class? _____

_____

8. Why was Tom chosen as **'player of the match'**? _____

_____

_____

9. This story contains a number of terms which are used in cricket and in ballet. Do you know what these words or phrases mean?

barre   scored a century

pavilion   splits

took five wickets   pas de chat

Continued from P44

SCHOLASTIC **Photocopiable**

Name:

The Hare with many friends

A play is another way of telling a story. This play has a narrator (storyteller) and characters from the story. This story is a fable and so has a moral.

Before you read

You have probably heard the story of 'The Hare and the Tortoise'. Can you remember what kind of personality the hare had?

Read this play

THE HARE WITH MANY FRIENDS

A Hare is running away from a pack of hounds, who are heard throughout the play baying and barking in the background. The noise of the hounds gets louder as the play proceeds.

NARRATOR: Hare had always thought he was popular with the other animals. Then one sunny day, he heard a pack of hounds. He realised that they were coming his way and so rushed off to seek help from his friends. The first friend he met was Bull.

HARE: I'm so glad I've found you, Bull. Those hounds are after me. I want you to charge at them and frighten them with your horns.

BULL: I'm very sorry, Hare, I have to meet someone. But I feel sure that our friend Goat will do what you want.

NARRATOR: Hare ran off to find Goat, who was eating some flowers.

HARE: Quick, my good friend Goat. The hounds are after me and I need your help. I want you to butt those awful hounds when they reach here. I'll just jump up on your back to be out of the way.

GOAT: No, don't do that, Hare. I don't think I can help. I've had a bad back and I don't think it would be helped if you jumped up there.

NARRATOR: Hare, by this time, was getting very worried that none of his friends really seemed to want to help, but he knew Ram wouldn't let him down. He found him grazing in a field near the stream.

HARE: Ram, I need your help and I need it now. Can you hear the pack of hounds that is after me?

RAM: Oh Hare, I really feel I can't. Hounds, you know, are just as likely to eat sheep as hares.

NARRATOR: Finally, Hare went off to find Calf. He realised that this friend was his last hope.

HARE: Calf, please, please can you help me? Nobody else is able to and I don't know where else to turn.

CALF: I'd like to, Hare. But if the others, who are so much bigger and stronger, can't help, how can I be of any use? Ask someone else.

(The Hare darts backwards and forwards to the sound of the hounds coming closer.)

NARRATOR: The hounds were now very close. Hare ran as fast as he could into the deepest part of the forest, where he found a safe place to hide. (*The sound of the hounds gradually dies away. The Hare drops down exhausted.*) Luckily, the hounds missed him, but as he lay there panting, he murmured, "So much for friends."

Continued on P47

Re-read the play ▶ **Answer the following questions.**

1. Why was Hare in danger? _____ |

_____

2. Which characters in the play did Hare think of as friends? _Give all of them_ ___ |

_____

3. What did Hare want Bull to do? _____ |

_____

4. Why was Calf his last chance of a friend helping him? _____ |

_____

5. Why didn't Hare just run off at the start of the play as he did at the end? _____

_____ 2

6. Why do you think his friends refused to help him? Were all their excuses truthful? _____

_____ 2

_____

7. Do you feel sorry for Hare? Why? _____

_____ 2

_____

8. Which animal do you think would have been most useful in protecting Hare from the hounds? Why?

_____

_____

9. What does the narrator do in the story? How important is this role? _____

_____

_____

More things to do ▶ 'The Hare and the Tortoise' is a well-known fable. With a group of friends, turn the fable into a play.

Continued from ▶ P46

The storm

In a play the story is developed by characters saying things. This is called dialogue. A play also has suggestions about where the scene is set and what the characters are doing or feeling. These are called stage directions.

Before you read

- Do you remember any bad thunderstorms? How did you feel?
- What should you do if you are caught outside in a thunderstorm?

Read this play

THE STORM

Matthew and his sister Kirsty have been to the cinema and are hurrying to get home before a big storm breaks. They have no coats. The sky has become very dark. Loud thunder is heard as the play begins. The weather has changed suddenly and the children are feeling cold and frightened.

MATTHEW: Come on, Kirsty. Can't you go any faster? We'll be caught in this storm. I knew I shouldn't have taken you with me today.

KIRSTY: Matthew, wait for me. I just can't go any faster. How long have we got before the rain starts?

MATTHEW: How am I supposed to know that?! (*Lightning flashes very close to them followed by loud thunder. A strong wind begins to blow and drops of rain begin to fall.*) Run Kirsty, run! See if we can make it to that tall tree.

KIRSTY: But Matthew… you're not supposed to… OK.

(They begin to run, but the rain is pelting down. They are soon soaked through and the tree still seems a long way off. As they approach a corner, an old lady appears. Her umbrella is blown inside out.)

OLD LADY: Children, children, you must get inside and out of this terrible storm. Come into my house till it blows over. You'll be safe there.

(Matthew keeps on running but Kirsty stops.)

KIRSTY: Matthew, come back. This lady says we can go into her house until the storm has passed. Matthew! Matthew!

(Matthew doesn't stop running. The storm is so noisy that he can't hear Kirsty. Suddenly the old lady takes out a whistle and blows it loudly. Matthew stops, looks around and sees his little sister going into a house with a stranger. He races back towards them. Just as he reaches them, there is a huge flash of lightning and a deafening crack of thunder.)

OLD LADY: Come on, my boy. Come through into the hall, or at least inside the porch. Good gracious me! Just look at that!

(Matthew and Kirsty look where the old lady is pointing. The tree they had been running to has been hit by lightning.)

MATTHEW: (*very shakily*) I was running to get under that big tree. Look at it now. If I… if we… had been standing there, we wouldn't have had a chance!

(He opens his mouth to say something else but another clap of thunder drowns him out. The storm then seems to be passing.)

Continued on P49

KIRSTY: It's so lucky that we stopped, I can tell you.
     (*She looks down and finds she is holding the old lady's hand. She is still trembling.*)

OLD LADY: You should never shelter under a tree during a storm. Remember, never, never! Come inside and I'll ring your parents so they can come and pick you up. Then I'll make a nice cup of tea. I think we all need one!

Re-read the play   **Answer the following questions.**

1. Where had Matthew and Kirsty been? _____

2. How were they caught out in the thunderstorm? _____

_____

3. Who made the decision to shelter under the tall tree? _____

_____

4. How did the old lady stop Matthew? _____

_____

5. Why do you think the old lady was carrying a whistle? _____

_____

6. Why was the old lady's umbrella turned inside out? _____

_____

7. How did the children feel as they saw the smouldering tree? _____

_____

8. If you were playing the part of Kirsty, what would you tell your parents when they arrived to collect you?

_____

_____

_____

More things to do   Imagine you are Matthew or Kirsty. Tell the story of your storm adventure. Try to make clear how you felt.

Continued from P48

Photocopiable

Brer Rabbit and the tar baby

This play is based on a story about the trickster, Brer Rabbit. It is about a clever hero (Brer Rabbit) who outwits his old enemy (Brer Fox). These stories were first told in the southern part of the United States.

Before you read

- If you were captured by an enemy, can you think of a way to trick him so that you could escape?
- What do you think a tar baby is?

Read this play

BRER RABBIT AND THE TAR BABY

Brer Fox has been trying to catch Brer Rabbit for a long time. He has now made a tar baby and placed it on the road. Brer Rabbit walks towards it.

BRER RABBIT: Good morning! Nice morning ain't it?
　　　　　　　(There is no answer.)

BRER RABBIT: You deaf or something? I said, Good morning.
　　　　　　　(He waits for an answer but none comes.)

BRER RABBIT: You just have no manners. I'll teach you some.
　　　　　　　(He thumps the tar baby but his hand sticks to the tar.)

BRER RABBIT: Hey! What are you doing! Let go! I've got another fist, you know. I'll thump you with that if you don't let go.
　　　　　　　(He thumps the tar baby with his other fist. It sticks, too.)

BRER RABBIT: Let go! *(He kicks the tar baby and his foot sticks.)* All right, you asked for it!

　　(He kicks with his other foot, then head-butts the tar baby. He is completely stuck. Brer Fox appears.)

BRER FOX: Got you at last, Brer Rabbit. Now, let me think, what's the best way to finish you off? Umm! I think I'll light a fire and roast you.

BRER RABBIT: Roast me if you like, Brer Fox, but please, please don't throw me into that blackberry bush.

BRER FOX: Guess I can't roast you Brer Rabbit. Ain't got no wood. I think I'll just string you up from that tree.

BRER RABBIT: String me up if you like, Brer Fox, but please, please don't throw me into that blackberry bush.

BRER FOX: Guess I can't string you up, Brer Rabbit. Ain't got no rope. Guess I might just throw you into that blackberry bush.

BRER RABBIT: No, Brer Fox! No!

　　(Brer Fox lifts Brer Rabbit and the sticky tar baby and throws them into the blackberry bush.)

BRER FOX: Take that, you pesky rabbit. Now I'm rid of you for ever.

　　(There is silence for a moment, then a voice is heard humming a little tune.)

BRER RABBIT: Tum-te-tum. Thanks a lot, Brer Fox. This prickly blackberry bush is just the thing to get rid of the sticky tar. I'll see you around!

Continued on P51

Re-read the play → **Answer the following questions.**

1. What had Brer Fox been doing for a long time? _____

_____

2. Why didn't Brer Fox roast Brer Rabbit? _____

_____

3. What did Brer Rabbit keep telling Brer Fox not to do? _____

_____

4. Do you think Brer Fox was very bright? Why? _____

_____

_____

5. What sort of character do you think Brer Rabbit was? _____

_____

_____

6. Write a final speech for Brer Fox once he finds out he has been tricked. _____

_____

_____

_____

7. Write something Brer Rabbit might have said in reply. _____

_____

_____

8. What do you think these words mean?

trickster _____

Brer _____

pesky _____

Continued from P50

Our trip to Shingle Cove

A recount describes something that happened in the past, such as the events of a holiday. This recount is about what happened on a trip to a seaside town.

Before you read

- Where did you go for your last holiday?
- Think of three things that you did while you were there.

Read this recount

OUR TRIP TO SHINGLE COVE

During the summer holidays we went on a trip to Shingle Cove, a small town near the sea. Mum, Dad and I went, and my friend Jody. We stayed in a cottage for a week.

Every morning we walked to the beach for a swim. On some days the water was rough, but on other days it was calm. Jody and I used to race down the beach and jump into the sea!

Some afternoons, Dad, Jody and I played golf at a course near the end of the beach. Dad can hit the ball a really long way. Jody and I only ever managed to beat him on one hole, and it was short.

While we were away, Mum spent the afternoons reading her book. She said she enjoyed the peace!

One day Jody and I found a secret path to the beach. We had to scramble through some gorse and down a rocky track. It was a bit scary at times and we had to be careful. We got to the beach long before Mum and Dad. They went along the road and took ages.

In the evenings we sometimes had a barbecue, then afterwards we would sit on the patio and look out over the sea. If the weather wasn't warm we would play cards on the table inside. Jody and I never wanted to go to bed.

We were all very sad when we had to go home. I really liked Shingle Cove. I hope we can go back there again next year.

Re-read the recount   **Answer the following questions.**

1. Where did the writer go during the holidays? _____

_____

2. What did the children do each morning? _____

_____

Continued on P53

3. How did the two children get to the beach before Mum and Dad? _____

_____

4. What did they do in the evenings after dinner? _____

_____

5. Do you think the writer's mum liked golf? Why? Why not? _____

_____

6. Do you think the cottage was at sea level or on a slope high above the sea? _____

_____

_____

7. Do you think the writer is a boy or a girl? What are your reasons for thinking that? _____

_____

_____

_____

8. Are there any things that the writer did on holiday which you would enjoy doing? _____

_____

_____

9. What sort of holidays do you like best – camping holidays, trips overseas, beach holidays or another type?

_____

_____

10. What do you think is important on holiday if you are to have a good time?

_____

_____

_____

More things to do Write a recount of a holiday you have enjoyed.

Continued from P52

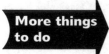 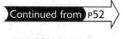

Flat Stanley

This recount is about a book the writer has just finished reading. Like any recount, it is about something that happened in the past.

Before you read

Tell a friend about a book you read recently. Start by giving the title of the book, and the author's name, too, if you can remember it. Try to tell at least three things you remember about the book.

Read this recount

FLAT STANLEY

Today I read a book called *Flat Stanley*. It was a really funny book about a boy who was flat!

Stanley Lambchop was flattened by a bulletin board that fell on his bed. He was not hurt, but he was flat – about 15 millimetres thick.

While he was flat he was able to do some unusual things: he was posted to California for a holiday, he went down a grating in the street to find Mrs Lambchop's ring and he was flown as a kite by his brother, Arthur.

His best adventure was when he helped to capture a gang of thieves who had been stealing famous paintings. He did this by pretending to be a picture on the wall.

If you read this very funny book by Jeff Brown yourself, you can find out just how it happened!

Re-read the recount   **Answer the following questions.**

1. What was the name of the book? Who was the author? _____

_____

2. How was Stanley made flat? _____

_____

3. Where did Stanley go on holiday while he was flat? _____

_____

Continued on P55

4. What was Stanley's best adventure? _____

_____

5. Who do you think Mrs Lambchop might be? _____

_____

6. Stanley helped to capture a gang of thieves by pretending to be a picture on the wall. Why would the thieves have thought he was a picture?

_____

7. What type of books do you think this writer enjoys? _____

_____

8. At the end of the story, Stanley gets sick of being flat. How do you think he is made his normal shape again?

_____

_____

9. What information in this recount makes you think that Flat Stanley is an imaginary story?

_____

_____

10. What advantages and disadvantages would there be to being flat? Write two short paragraphs – one in favour of being flat, the other presenting the case against being flat.

_____

_____

_____

_____

_____

_____

_____

_____

_____

Continued from P54

How to catch a train

Instructions provide step-by-step information on how to complete a task as well as a list of what you need.

Before you read

- Have you ever caught a train?
- Where was the train going to?

Read these instructions

HOW TO CATCH A TRAIN

You will need:
A single or return train ticket to your destination.
A train timetable.

What to do:
1. Choose destination.
2. Choose date and time of travel.
3. Look through timetable to find suitable train.
4. Make sure you arrive at station in plenty of time.
5. Check timetable displayed in station to make sure of:
    - time train leaves;
    - which platform train leaves from;
    - stations where train stops (make sure station you want is included).
6. Buy ticket (if you have not already bought it). Keep it with you at all times as it may be checked.
7. Walk to platform.
8. Wait for train. Do not stand too near edge of platform.
9. Wait until train stops and doors open.
10. Step into train. Move away from doorways.
11. Find seat if possible.
12. Watch out for station that is the one before your station.
13. Stay in your seat until the train stops, then go to the doors.
14. Keep well back until doors open.
15. Step out on to platform and move away from edge.

Re-read the instructions

Answer the following questions.

1. What type of ticket might you buy to ride on the train? _____

_____

2. Why do you need to hold on to your ticket? _____

_____

3. What three pieces of information do you need before you catch the train? _____

_____

Continued on P57

 **SCHOLASTIC** Photocopiable

4. Why do you need to stand away from the edge of the platform as the train comes into the station?

_____

_____

5. Why is it important to know the name of the station before the one where you want to get off?

_____

_____

6. Why should you keep clear of the doorways? _____

_____

7. If you do not find a seat on the train, what should you do? _____

_____

8. Number the following instructions in the correct order.

Move to platform to catch train. ☐   Ask for ticket to destination. ☐

Check you have enough money. ☐   Hand over money for ticket. ☐

Wait for ticket. ☐   Decide if you want single or return ticket. ☐

9. If you could take a train trip to anywhere in the world, where would you go? Why?

_____

_____

_____

10. Instructions often have words left out of sentences. Write out steps 8 and 15 but include all the words that have been left out.

_____

_____

_____

More things to do ➤ Write a set of instructions explaining how to catch your local bus or how to get ready for school in the morning. Look closely at the steps in the instructions on the previous page.

Continued from ▷ P56 ⟩

📖 SCHOLASTIC ▷Photocopiable◁

How to grow tomatoes

Instructions tell you how something is done. You need to know the materials that are needed and the steps you must take.

Before you read ➤

Have you ever planted and grown something? Can you remember two things you had to do to make the plant grow?

Read these instructions ➤

HOW TO GROW TOMATOES

Materials
small container of tomato plants
space in a garden
fertiliser
water
support canes
string

Steps
1. Separate tomato plants.
2. Plant them in garden (40cm apart).
3. Place support cane beside each plant.
4. Water plants immediately.
5. As plants grow, tie each one to cane with string.
6. Apply fertiliser at regular intervals.
7. Water plants daily.
8. Pick tomatoes when ripe.

Re-read the instructions ➤ **Answer the following questions.**

1. Name three things you need to grow tomatoes. _____

_____

_____

2. Where do you plant the tomatoes? _____

_____

Continued on P59 ➤

3. How often do you need to water the tomatoes? _____

_____

4. What would happen if the plants were:

   ● not fertilised _____

   ● not watered? _____

5. Why do you need to place canes beside the plants? _____

_____

6. Why should you pick the tomatoes when they are ripe? _____

_____

7. How do you know when a tomato is ripe? _____

_____

8. What else do tomatoes need to grow (other than the items listed under **Materials**)?

_____

_____

9. Some people spray tomatoes. Why do they do this? _____

_____

_____

10. Why do some people disagree with spraying vegetables in gardens? _____

_____

_____

More things to do

Grow your own tomatoes. You may be able to grow one tomato plant in a pot, or ask if you can use a bit of garden at home or at school (or a tub or window box). You could try growing some herbs (like parsley) and some vegetables too.

Continued from P58

SCHOLASTIC Photocopiable

Catching a fish

An instruction tells you how to do something. These instructions tell you the things you need and the steps you should take to try to catch a fish.

Before you read ▶

Talk to a friend about how you would catch a fish.

Read these instructions ▶

CATCHING A FISH

Materials
fishing line
landing net
hooks
knife
weights
keepnet
bait

Steps
1. Tie hook and weight to line and cut loose ends with knife.
2. Fix bait onto hook.
3. Cast line with baited hook from boat, bank, wharf or beach.
4. Wind in loose line.
5. Wait for fish to bite.
6. Pull in fish when hooked.
7. Net fish in water and lift out.
8. Unhook fish and place in keepnet (so that the fish can be returned to the water later).

Re-read the instructions ▶ **Answer the following questions.**

1. Name three things you need to catch a fish. _____

_____

2. Where do you put the bait? _____

_____

Continued on P61 ▶

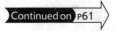

3. Where do you put the fish after you have caught it in the net? _____

_____

4. Why would you wind in any loose line? _____

_____

5. Why would you use a weight? _____

_____

_____

6. Why do you net the fish in the water instead of pulling it out on the line? _____

_____

_____

7. If you caught a very small fish, what would you do with it? _____

_____

8. What is bait? _____

_____

9. What is the meaning of **cast** in step 3? _____

_____

_____

10. Why is it important to be very quiet and patient when you are fishing? _____

_____

_____

_____

More things to do

- Write some instructions on how to catch tadpoles. Remember to write what you will need, where you will go and any other information, including what to do with the ones you catch.
- There may be children in your class who have gone fishing. Ask them to tell you more about how it is done.

Continued from P60

Sports day

A report begins with a statement of what its subject is, then gives a number of facts about it.

Before you read

- What can you remember about your last school sports day?
- Which events do you enjoy most on sports day? Why?

Read this report

HIGHVIEW SPORTS DAY

Highview School Sports Day was held last Friday. The weather was fine and nearly everyone in the school was there. The three Houses – Blue, Yellow and Red – each tried hard to gain the most points and win the House trophy.

For a long time Red was leading, with Blue second. Near the end of the afternoon, Blue won a number of relay races and in the end finished ahead by five points. Congratulations Blue House!

The top-scoring girl athlete was Ashi Khan in Year 5. She won the 100 metres sprint, the skipping race and was in the winning girls' relay team from Blue House.

Fergus Thomas was the top-scoring boy. He won the 100 metres sprint and the cross-country race as well.

The egg-and-spoon race and the sack race were both won by the Yellow team. They said that they had the most fun on the day.

Re-read the report

Answer the following questions.

1. Which House won the trophy? _____

2. Which girl scored the most points? _____

3. Who was the champion boy athlete? _____

4. Which House won the egg-and-spoon race and had the most fun? _____

_____

Continued on P63

 SCHOLASTIC Photocopiable

5. Do you think Yellow House took the day as seriously as the other Houses? Why? _____

_____

_____

6. The sports day was popular in the school. How do you know that? _____

_____

_____

7. If you had a choice, which House would you have liked to be in? Why? _____

_____

_____

_____

8. Reports contain many facts. Write down four facts from this report. _____

_____

_____

_____

_____

9. Do you have Houses in your school? What are they called and which one are you in?

_____

_____

10. What sort of person would you need to be, and what sort of things would you need to do, if you wanted to be a top athlete?

_____

_____

_____

_____

More things to do ➤ Write a report about your sports day or about another sporting event that you have attended.

Continued from **P62**

SCHOLASTIC Photocopiable

Name:

The elephant

A report gives us information about something. It begins by telling the reader what the report is about. It then gives facts that provide much more detail about the subject.

Before you read

- Many wild animals today are endangered. Do you know what an endangered species is?
- What might cause a species to be endangered?

Read this report

THE ELEPHANT

Elephants are the largest land animals in the world. They live in Africa and the south of Asia.

There are two kinds of elephant – African and Indian. African elephants are bigger than Indian elephants. They often weigh five or six tonnes, and can be even more! It is easy to tell the difference between the two types. African elephants have sloping foreheads and very large ears. They are also darker in colour.

Elephants eat plants, fruit and the young shoots of trees, using their amazing noses, or trunks, to put food into their mouths. They also use their trunks for drinking. Water is sucked up by the trunk and is then squirted into the mouth. Elephants drink a lot of water, often more than 100 litres in a day.

Elephants use their trunks to lift things. They are very strong and can pull and carry big loads. They often live for about 50 years, a long life for an animal.

Sad to say, these wonderful animals are under threat in the wild. They are hunted for their tusks, which are made of ivory and are therefore very valuable.

However, plastics and other materials can now often be used instead of ivory, and wild elephants are protected in many parts of the world. It is hoped that, in time, their numbers will increase.

Re-read the report

Answer the following questions.

1. Where do elephants live? _____

_____

2. How would you tell the difference between the two types of elephant? _____

_____

Continued on P65

SCHOLASTIC Photocopiable

3. What are two uses the elephant has for its trunk? _____

_____

4. Why are elephants hunted and killed? _____

_____

5. Elephants are sometimes tamed and used by people. What might they be used for?

_____

_____

6. What two facts give us hope that elephants will increase in number? Why is this important?

_____

_____

_____

7. What is ivory used for? _____

_____

8. Elephants are not the only endangered species in our world. What would you do to help endangered animals and birds if you could?

_____

_____

_____

_____

9. Write three facts from this report that you find the most interesting. _____

_____

_____

_____

_____

More things to do

- Find out some more facts about elephants.
- Find out about the white rhinoceros or another endangered species. Write a report about it.

Continued from P64

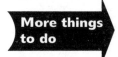

The earthworm

A report starts by stating what its subject is, then it gives many interesting facts. This report is about earthworms – what they look like, how they live and the important part they play in the natural world.

Before you read

Find an earthworm or a picture of one. Look at it very closely and write down three facts about it.

Read this report

THE EARTHWORM

Earthworms are long, round animals that live in moist, rich soil.

They have no spine, legs or feet. Their pinkish brown bodies are made up of rings or segments that are covered with tiny hairs called setae. These hairs help the worms to move along.

Earthworms spend most of their lives underground. They feed on soil that contains decaying animal or plant matter.

Earthworms burrow into the earth with their blunt heads, eating large amounts of soil as they go. They digest it in their bodies and leave the waste on top of the ground in little heaps, called worm casts.

Earthworms help to make the earth fertile. They enrich it with their waste, and they also loosen it as they burrow through the ground. The passages they create allow air and water to enter the soil.

Animals, birds and fish all eat worms, which form an important part of their food. So anywhere you find worms, you will also find birds, animals, plants and rich soil. Earthworms are therefore very important creatures.

Re-read the report   **Answer the following questions.**

1. Give three facts about the earthworm's appearance. _____

_____

_____

_____

2. What do earthworms eat? _____

_____

Continued on **P67**

3. Where do earthworms live? _____

4. What is a worm cast? _____

_____

5. How do earthworms help to make the soil fertile? _____

_____

_____

6. If there were lots of earthworms in your garden, what would you know about the soil there?

_____

_____

7. What might happen to the soil if there were no earthworms? _____

_____

8. Do you think that people should try to protect earthworms? _____

_____

_____

9. What do these words mean?

moist _____

_____

setae _____

_____

decaying _____

_____

10. How could you help to make your soil a more suitable place for earthworms to live in?

_____

_____

More things to do

- Bring in some earthworms in a jar. Study them and write your own report.
- Draw a picture of an earthworm. Show its segments and its blunt head.

Continued from P66

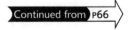

How a rainbow is made

An explanation gives you reasons why or how things work or are the way they are. It begins with a general statement about the object or process.

Before you read

- When do you see a rainbow?
- Name any three colours you see in a rainbow.

Read this explanation

HOW A RAINBOW IS MADE

A rainbow is a coloured arch that appears in the sky when it is raining or there is rain about. A rainbow is made up of seven colours.

Our light comes from the Sun. When the Sun is shining it is daytime; when it is not shining it is night-time.

The light we see is made up of many colours, but when these colours are mixed up together, they appear as white light. The colours are red, orange, yellow, green, blue, indigo and violet.

A rainbow is formed when light hits raindrops and the drops of water split the particles of white light up into different coloured parts. As both raindrops and light are needed to make a rainbow, we are most likely to see rainbows in the sky on rainy days when the Sun shines through the clouds. The seven colours we see are called the light spectrum.

The seven colours of the light spectrum can be seen at other times. If you have ever blown bubbles you may remember that the rainbow colours also appear around the bubbles. This is because the skin of the bubble also breaks up the light.

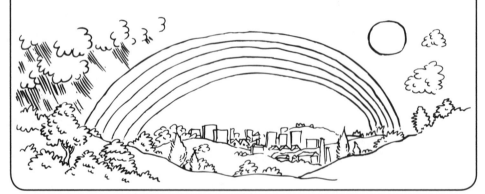

Re-read the explanation

Answer the following questions.

1. On what sort of day might you see a rainbow? _____

_____

2. Why is the Sun shining on the raindrops important in making a rainbow? _____

_____

_____

Continued on P69

SCHOLASTIC Photocopiable

3. What are the seven colours that make up the spectrum? _____

_____

4. Where does white light come from? _____

_____

5. Why can't you see a rainbow at night? _____

_____

6. What sort of colours are indigo and violet? _____

_____

7. Can you think of any other times when you might see all the colours of the rainbow together?

_____

_____

8. Draw a rainbow on the back of this sheet and label the colours that are found in it.

9. A rainbow can give you a clue to the type of weather that is around you or near to you. Can you think of any other things you might notice around you that may indicate changes in the weather?

_____

_____

_____

_____

10. A rainbow is sometimes seen as a symbol of hope. Why do you think this is? _____

_____

_____

_____

_____

More things to do

There is an old saying that there is a pot of gold hidden at the end of the rainbow. Have you ever tried to reach the end of a rainbow? Why is it not possible?

Continued from P68

How we digest our food

An explanation explains how something works or why something happens. First it gives an overall statement about the subject it is explaining. It then lists a number of points to explain the process.

Before you read

- Do you know the meaning of the word **digest**? If not, look it up in your dictionary.
- Why do you think we need to chew our food well?

Read this explanation

HOW WE DIGEST OUR FOOD

General statement
The food we eat has to be changed into many things, including muscles, bones, blood and energy. This process is called digestion.

Points that explain
First, the food is chewed and mixed with saliva in the mouth. Then it is swallowed and goes into the stomach.

In the stomach, the food is mixed with gastric juices. It is then sent to the small intestine where it is mixed again with bile from the liver. This helps to digest the fats.

Digestive juices from the pancreas break down the starch and sugar.

As the pulp (the digesting food) moves along the small intestine, the nutrients (the important building blocks of the body) are absorbed into the bloodstream. What is left is passed into the large intestine and finally out of the body.

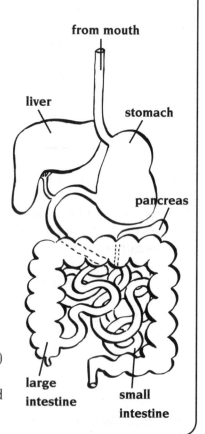

from mouth

liver

stomach

pancreas

large intestine

small intestine

Re-read the explanation

Answer the following questions.

1. When food is chewed, what is mixed with it? _____

2. Where does the chewed food go once it is swallowed? _____

_____

3. Where does bile come from? _____

4. What are nutrients? _____

_____

Continued on P71

SCHOLASTIC Photocopiable

5. Is all the food we eat used in the body during digestion? How do you know? _____

_____

_____

6. If you eat too much at once, why might you feel sick or have stomach-ache? _____

_____

_____

7. Why do we need to eat a varied diet? _____

_____

_____

8. What types of foods do we need to eat in order to keep fit and healthy? _____

_____

_____

9. What does **bloodstream** mean? _____

_____

10. This explanation has a labelled diagram beside it. Why is this useful in helping us to understand how we digest our food?

_____

_____

More things to do ▶ Draw a labelled diagram of a mouth. Label the teeth, lips, tongue, throat and salivary glands.

Continued from **P70** ▷

Why an iceberg floats

An explanation gives reasons why or how something works or is the way it is. It begins with a general statement about the process or the object.

Before you read

- What is an iceberg made out of?
- Where would you find icebergs?

Read this explanation

WHY AN ICEBERG FLOATS

An iceberg is really just a giant ice cube and, just like an ice cube in a glass of lemonade, it floats.

But why does it float?

Ice is frozen water. If you put water into a freezer it will, after a few hours, turn into ice. When it turns to ice, it expands or gets bigger.

If a milk bottle is left on the doorstep in winter, the milk may freeze, expand and push the foil cap off the bottle. This is because the milk has changed into ice.

Why does water expand as it changes into ice?

Ice is made up of very fine crystals. These crystals take up more space and so the liquid expands. The ice that is formed is also not as heavy as the same amount of water. So it floats.

If you look at an ice cube floating in lemonade, you will notice that the ice only just rises above the surface. Icebergs are the same. Only one-ninth of an iceberg shows above the surface. So that means that eight-ninths of it are completely hidden below the water.

This means that if the iceberg you see rises 10 metres above the sea, there is another 80 metres below the surface, so the whole block of ice is 90 metres high. That's as tall as many office buildings.

Re-read the explanation

Answer the following questions.

1. Does an ice cube float? _____

2. What is ice made of? _____

3. Where do you make ice in your home? _____

_____

Continued on **P73**

SCHOLASTIC Photocopiable

4. How much of an iceberg is submerged beneath the surface of the sea? _____

_____

5. What would happen to a bottle of wine if you left it in the freezer for a long time? _____

_____

_____

6. What happens when water changes to ice? _____

_____

7. 'Why an iceberg floats' is an explanation and therefore starts with a general statement about icebergs. What is an iceberg compared with and why did the writer use the comparison? Do you think it is a useful comparison?

_____

_____

_____

8. Mark whether these sentences are true or false.

Icebergs are much smaller than they appear to be. _____

Icebergs float because ice is not as heavy as water. _____

Ice is really crystallised water. _____

9. ● If you saw an iceberg rising 20 metres above the sea, how much would be below the surface?

_____

  ● How high would the iceberg be? _____

10. Why could icebergs be dangerous to ships? _____

_____

_____

_____

More things to do

● Draw a diagram of an iceberg floating in the sea. Show the part above the surface and the part below the surface.
● Where do icebergs come from and how do they come to be floating around the seas? Write a short explanation, using the passage as a model.

Continued from P72

Why some spiders have webs

An explanation explains why or how something works or is the way it is. It begins with a general statement about the object or the process.

Before you read

- Where have you found spiders' webs?
- What have you noticed about these webs?
- Have you ever found anything in them?

Read this explanation

WHY SOME SPIDERS HAVE WEBS

A spider's web is its home, its supermarket and its pantry. The web is used as a place to live, and a place to catch and store food.

Spiders start building their webs with a single strand of spider silk. Once this first strand has been fastened at both ends, the spider spins the next strand. Each kind of spider makes its very own kind of web.

Many spiders make a circular web; they are then able to run along the strands that come out from the centre. The strands of the web that go around the circle are sticky, so that any insects that touch these are caught and become a meal for the spider. Some spiders even lay their eggs inside these insects. Then, when the eggs hatch, there is a ready supply of food for the baby spiders to eat.

Once a spider has built its web, it sits in the middle, waiting for insects to fly into its trap. When an insect becomes stuck to the web, it begins to struggle. This movement lets the spider know it is there. The spider can then go quickly to the prey and kill it.

Spiders' webs are a very important part of how a spider lives. So, next time you think about knocking down a spider's web that is not really hurting anyone, take a moment to think about the time, effort and care that has gone into building that web. You wouldn't want your shelter, or your way of getting food, taken away from you, would you?

Re-read the explanation

Answer the following questions.

1. How does a spider begin to build its web? _____

_____

2. If a spider builds a circular web, what use does it make of the strands that come out from the centre?

_____

_____

Continued on P75

3. What is different about the strands that run around the web? _____

_____

4. How does the spider know that it has trapped an insect in its web? _____

_____

5. What does it do with trapped insects? _____

_____

6. Use the information in this passage to draw, and label, a diagram of a spider's web on the back of this sheet.

7. In the first paragraph, a spider's web is compared with several things that are a regular part of human life. Why did the writer do this?

_____

_____

_____

8. A spider's web could also be compared to a net. Would that be a good comparison? Why?

_____

_____

_____

9. Mark these sentences either true or false.

Spiders' webs are sticky. _____

All spiders spin webs. _____

All spiders' webs are the same. _____

10. What do these words mean?

prey _____

pantry _____

More things to do Are you afraid of spiders? Why do you think so many people dislike them? Write a short paragraph giving your explanation.

Continued from P74

A varied diet is best

An argument states a point of view, then makes several statements which support this. It sums up at the end.

Before you read

- Think of some foods that are good for you.
- What are some of your favourite foods?

Read this argument

A VARIED DIET IS BEST

Humans need to eat different kinds of foods if they are to have a balanced diet. If they do this, they will grow fit and strong, have plenty of energy and enjoy good health.

Some foods provide us with proteins which make the body grow. Some foods are rich in carbohydrates or fats; these give us energy. Other foods are rich in vitamins and minerals; they help to keep us fit and well.

No one food can supply all the things we need. That is why it is important to eat a wide range of foods.

We need to eat foods like meat, fish, nuts, eggs and cheese for proteins; we should include grains, sugar and fats to give us energy; it is also important to eat fruit and vegetables for minerals and vitamins.

If we include these foods, and others, in our meals then we can be sure that we are eating a varied and balanced diet.

Re-read the argument

Answer the following questions.

1. Why does your body need proteins? _____

_____

2. Give the names of at least three foods that are rich in proteins. _____

_____

3. Why do we need to eat foods that contain vitamins and minerals? _____

_____

Continued on P77

 ■SCHOLASTIC **Photocopiable**

4. Why is it important to have a varied and balanced diet? _____

_____

5. If, for lunch, you had wholemeal bread sandwiches with cheese or chicken as a filling, fresh fruit and a glass of milk, do you think that lunch would be good for you? Why?

_____

_____

_____

6. Would this writer think that a packet of potato crisps and a fizzy drink would be a good lunch? Why?

_____

_____

7. What is the point of view put forward in this argument? Do you agree with it? _____

_____

_____

_____

8. What do you usually have for your lunch? Would the writer think it was a healthy lunch? Why?

_____

_____

_____

9. If you wanted to eat a healthy snack between meals, what would you choose? Why?

_____

_____

10. Why do some people eat food that is not good for them? _____

_____

_____

More things to do

In your group, have a discussion about good diet. You may not agree with all of the points in the argument above.

Continued from P76

SCHOLASTIC Photocopiable

Team games are more fun

An argument states a point of view. Then it gives points which argue for this view. It sums up the case at the end.

Before you read

- What games do you like to play?
- What team games do you play or watch?

Read this argument

TEAM GAMES ARE MORE FUN

Team games are much better than games you have to play by yourself. They allow more people to play, so you are able to play with your friends.

In order to win a team game, the players have to work together. This develops character and teaches people to be unselfish.

Playing in team games gives you pride in your school or club. It is a great feeling to know that you have done your best for your team – games that you play by yourself do not produce team spirit.

So, as well as helping people to learn how to be part of a team, team games are just much more fun. And if your side wins, so much the better!

Re-read the argument

Answer the following questions.

1. What is the writer's point of view about team games? _____

_____

_____

_____

2. What do the players have to do if they wish to win a team game? _____

_____

Continued on P79

3. The writer makes some important points to conclude the argument. What are they?

_____

_____

_____

4. In what way would playing team games make you unselfish? _____

_____

_____

5. How do you feel if you play well for your team? _____

_____

6. Do you think playing team games would help you to make friends? Give one or two reasons to support your argument.

_____

_____

_____

_____

7. Can you name two team games? _____

_____

8. Can you think of two games you can play by yourself? _____

_____

9. Explain the meaning of:

develops character _____

_____

team spirit _____

_____

More things to do

- Think about team games you like to play. Say why you enjoy them. Write an argument about why you like to play your favourite game.
- Try to explain the rules and how to play your favourite game. Do this as if the person to whom you are explaining the game knows nothing about it (he or she doesn't know any technical terms). It may be harder than you think!

Continued from P78

Cats make good pets

A debate is a type of argument in which there are usually two sides, one for and one against the topic that is being discussed. In this debate the argument in favour is given first, followed by the argument against.

Before you read ▶

Think of one good thing and one bad thing about keeping a pet.

Read this argument ▶

CATS MAKE GOOD PETS

For

Cats make good pets because they are cuddly and beautiful. They are very clean as they look after their coats and always go to the toilet outside or in a litter tray.

Cats do not need a lot of food, and are usually not too fussy about what they eat. Most of all, cats make good pets because they like to be stroked. There is nothing nicer than hearing a happy cat purr.

Against

Cats do not make good pets because they scratch and spit when they are angry. They do not protect the house as dogs will and they often do not come when you call. You cannot take them for walks, and they hate riding in cars.

Worst of all, cats kill small birds and animals. These tiny creatures have no chance against a cat's sharp teeth and claws.

Re-read the argument ▶ **Answer the following questions.**

1. Write three reasons why cats make good pets. _____

_____

_____

2. Give three reasons against cats as pets. _____

_____

_____

Continued on P81 ▶

◼ SCHOLASTIC **Photocopiable**

3. What do cats do when they are angry? _____

4. What do cats do when they are happy? _____

5. What do you think is the best point in favour of cats as pets? _____

_____

_____

6. What do you think is the best point against the argument? _____

_____

_____

7. Which is the better argument in this debate, the case for or the case against? Why?

_____

_____

_____

8. In your opinion, what is the best pet to have? Give your reasons for keeping this kind of pet.

_____

_____

9. Some people keep strange creatures as pets. Write a case against keeping a snake as a pet.

_____

_____

10. Write the points for and against in a debate on 'Dogs make good pets'. _____

_____

_____

_____

_____

_____

More things to do ➤ Hold a debate in your class called 'Should we keep pets?'. There should be an equal number of speakers for and against, and one speaker on each side should sum up at the end. Ask everyone in the class to vote for one side or the other to see who won the debate.

Continued from P80 ⟩

Poetry

1 Door

Question types: 3 literal, 1 inferential, 3 evaluative, 2 deductive
1. The poet's grandmother's front door is being described in the poem.
2. The door was made of glass.
3. Answers may vary – the small reflections of light showed the colours of the rainbow.
4. They reminded the poet of fallen flowers.
5. Own answer.
6. Answers may vary – the poet is probably grown up, looking back to a time in her childhood.
7. Own answer.
8. Answers may vary – possibly in a church (stained glass).
9. Own answer.

2 Too early

Question types: 3 literal, 1 inferential, 2 evaluative, 4 deductive
1. Early to bed and early to rise makes a man healthy, wealthy and wise.
2. Birds eat worms.
3. The earliest bird, the one who gets up first, is best fed.
4. No, worms would be eaten if they got up early.
5. The early bird gets the worm.
6 and 7.   Own answers.
8. prosper – do well, thrive; sup – dine, eat, have a meal.
9. No, it suggests that the worms would be better to stay in bed.
10. Own answer.

3 Big black bird

Question types: 3 literal, 1 inferential, 2 evaluative, 3 deductive
1. The bird's eyes are yellow.
2. The bird's beak is black.
3. The bird's yellow eyes, size, long legs and black beak seem to worry the poet.
4. The poet's two excuses are that the bird might attack or it might fly away.
5. Answers may vary – it may be a blackbird, a crow or a raven.
6. Answers may vary – the poet is probably a child, as the bird seems very big and frightening.
7. The poet seems to be afraid of the bird, but is not keen to admit it outright.
8. In the second line of the poem the letter 'e's have been made to look like eyes; 'size', 'long', 'black', 'fly away' and 'distance' have been written so that the shape of the words matches their meaning; the block of colour for words like 'black' also helps to emphasise the meaning.
9. Own answer.

4 Me-moving

Question types: 3 literal, 2 inferential, 3 evaluative , 2 deductive
1. The title tells the reader that the poem is about the poet moving.
2. The poet darts, dashes, jigs, jumps, scampers, skates, scrambles, struts, strides, slips, slides and ambles.
3. amble; gambol.
4. Answers may vary – 'slip' and 'slide', 'crawl' and 'creep', 'rove' and 'ramble'.
5. Answers may vary – he ambles, crawls and creeps.
6. Three more groups of alliterative words are 'scamper', 'skate' and 'scramble'; 'strut' and 'stride'; and 'slip' and 'slide' ('leap' and 'lurch'; 'crawl' and 'creep'; 'rove', 'romp' and 'ramble'; 'turn' and 'trip'; and 'skid' and 'skip' are also correct answers).

7. You would not be able to crawl.
8. Own answer.
9. amble – move along in a slow, relaxed way; gambol – skip or jump about.
10. Own answer.

Narrative

5 **Theseus slays the Minotaur**

Question types: 2 literal, 3 inferential, 1 evaluative, 1 deductive
1. It was a monstrous creature who was half man and half bull; it ate human flesh; it lived in a labyrinth, a maze of passageways under the palace of the King of Crete.
2. Theseus was the son of King Aegeus of Athens. He followed the thread back to the gate.
3. A map is needed for this answer for the child to find Athens and Crete.
4. Answers may vary – he decided to go and kill the Minotaur even though he didn't have to.
5. He killed the monster with his bare hands.
6. They wouldn't have to supply any more people for the Minotaur to eat.
7. Own answer.

6 **Lauren and the flying dog (1)**

Question types: 4 literal, 1 inferential, 2 evaluative, 2 deductive
1. It was a horrible night and Lauren was afraid there was going to be a storm.
2. Mum insisted that Sheeba go out into the garage.
3. Lauren was in bed.
4. They shot out through the window.
5. They live in Scotland.
6. Lauren probably would have been frightened. She would not have expected anyone to have been outside her window at that time of night.
7. She was only wearing her pyjamas, and also they had been travelling at great speed and in a northerly direction.
8. Contests involving different Scottish activities, including dancing and sports, take place at a Highland Games.
9. It is a dance.

7 **Lauren and the flying dog (2)**

Question types: 3 literal, 3 inferential, 1 evaluative, 2 deductive
1. Lauren was going to meet Fifi and Pierre in Paris.
2. The name of the café is L'Ironique.
3. She joined in with the cancan.
4. Lauren was wearing a kilt (over her pyjamas).
5. She had been dancing and was out of breath.
6. She is referring to the English Channel.
7. A croissant is a bread-type roll, usually shaped like a crescent; it would probably be breakfast time.
8. Lauren wakes up at the end of the story; the adventure was a dream.
9. *cherie* – darling; *belle* – beautiful; *magnifique* – wonderful.

8 **Androcles and the lion**

Question types: 3 literal, 2 inferential, 2 evaluative, 3 deductive
1. Androcles saw a lion lying on the ground, moaning and groaning.
2. It had a thorn in its paw.
3. He pulled out the thorn and bandaged the paw.
4. The lion recognised Androcles as the man who had helped it.

5. No, the story is set in the past, probably in Roman times; clues include the words 'slave', 'Emperor' and 'arena' and the fact that throwing a person to the lions was used as a punishment.

6. Answers may vary – the Emperor came to watch what has happening to Androcles as a form of entertainment.

7. He could not believe that the lion had not attacked Androcles.

8. The crisis of the story was when the lion was about to eat Androcles.

9. If you help someone in trouble, then good will come back to you in the end.

10. filled with pity – felt very sorry; sprang to kill – leapt forward to kill (and eat).

 ## 9 The amazing Tamara Mudpuddle

Question types: 3 literal, 1 inferential, 2 evaluative, 3 deductive

1. She rose, like a hot-air balloon, until her head bumped against the ceiling.

2. Her grandfather had brought it back from Tibet.

3. No, she was always doing unusual things.

4. No, the trekking trip is referred to as recent.

5. Answers may vary – Tamara is imaginative, adventurous, rather unusual.

6. Answers may vary – they are probably fairly normal parents, quite dull, in fact, when compared with Tamara.

7. Answers may vary – floating to the ceiling could only take place in a fantasy story.

8. Tibet is a country in Asia; 'trekking' means going on a long journey on foot, perhaps in surroundings that make the journey difficult.

9. Own answer.

 ## 10 The lion and the mouse

Question types: 3 literal, 2 inferential, 1 evaluative, 1 deductive

1. The lion caught the mouse because he was angry with the mouse for waking him up.

2. He promised that if the lion let him go he would return the favour.

3. The hunters went away to collect a cart to carry the lion home.

4 and 5.   Answers may vary – select from choice of words.

6 and 7.   Own answers.

11 Julie of the Wolves

Question types: 5 literal, 2 inferential, 2 evaluative, 1 deductive

1. Miyax's father had become hungry on the hunting trip because he had seen no game – there had been nothing for him to kill and eat.

2. He had not explained to her how he had told the wolf that he needed food.

3. Miyax was trying to discover the sounds and movements that they made to express friendship.

4. She would then be able to tell the wolves that she was hungry and needed food.

5. They used signals to communicate.

6. She had managed to attract them by flicking her forefinger in the same way as they flicked their tails.

7. Answers may vary – Miyax's father had not returned from a seal-hunting trip; Miyax was hungry.

8–10. Own answers.

 ## 12 Tom

Question types: 5 literal, 1 inferential, 1 evaluative, 2 deductive

1. The ballet classes are held on Saturday mornings.

2. Tom had trainers on his feet.

3. He would have waited outside the cricket pavilion.

4. Tom is a good cricketer, he is good at batting, bowling and fielding, he plays every Saturday morning in summer with his team at the local cricket pitch.

5. He walks with his sister to her ballet school on his way to cricket.

6. Answers may vary – he may have been looking bored or he was in the way.

7. He joined in and had a go at everything they were doing; he didn't seem in a hurry to leave for his match – Jessica pointed to the clock to remind him of the time.

8. Answers may vary – he scored a century for his team; he batted, bowled and fielded very well.

9. barre – a horizontal, waist-height bar used for ballet exercises; splits – with the legs spread at right angles to the body; scored a century – made one hundred runs; took five wickets – responsible for dismissing five members of the opposing team; pavilion – a sports building used for changing or refreshments; *pas de chat* – a type of leap in ballet.

Drama

13 The Hare with many friends

Question types: 4 literal, 2 inferential, 2 evaluative, 1 deductive

1. Hare was being chased by a pack of hounds.

2. The characters he thought of as friends were Bull, Goat, Ram and Calf.

3. He wanted Bull to charge at the hounds and frighten them with his horns.

4. Answers may vary – nobody else had been able to help him, and he didn't know who else to ask; also, the hounds were now getting very close.

5. Answers may vary – he was sure he could rely on his friends to help him.

6. Answers may vary – they didn't like Hare as much as he thought, they couldn't be bothered to help him and they may have been afraid of the hounds themselves. His friends' replies were excuses, which weren't necessarily truthful.

7. Answers may vary – the reader may feel sorry for Hare because his friends let him down.

8. Answers may vary – Bull may have been the most useful in protecting the hare because of his horns and because he was the largest and most powerful animal.

9. The narrator keeps the story moving along and explains the action to the audience. In this play the narrator plays a very important part.

14 The storm

Question types: 4 literal, 1 inferential, 1 evaluative, 2 deductive

1. Matthew and Kirsty had been to the cinema.

2. When they were on their way home, the weather changed suddenly and they found themselves caught in the thunderstorm.

3. Matthew made the decision to shelter under the tall tree.

4. The old lady blew a whistle loudly.

5. Answers may vary – possibly to summon help if required, or to call a pet.

6. Her umbrella was turned inside out because the wind was blowing so hard.

7. They felt frightened, but thankful.

8. Own answer.

15 Brer Rabbit and the tar baby

Question types: 3 literal, 2 inferential, 2 evaluative, 1 deductive

1. Brer Fox had been trying to catch Brer Rabbit.

2. He had no wood.

3. Brer Rabbit kept telling Brer Fox not to throw him into the blackberry bush.

4. No, he should have suspected that Brer Rabbit was trying to trick him.

5. Answers may vary – Brer Rabbit was quick-witted and good at talking his way out of things.

6 and 7.   Own answer.

8. trickster – a clever person, good at fooling others; Brer – brother, a term of address; pesky – annoying, a nuisance.

Recount

 16 **Our trip to Shingle Cove**

Question types: 4 literal, 3 inferential, 1 evaluative, 2 deductive
1. The writer went to Shingle Cove, a small town near the sea.
2. The children went to the beach for a swim.
3. They scrambled through some gorse and down a rocky track.
4. They would sit and look out over the sea and sometimes they played cards.
5. Answers may vary – she probably just enjoyed some time on her own.
6. It was on a slope – they went down a path to the beach and were able to sit and look out over the sea.
7. Answers may vary – the writer's friend Jody could be a boy or a girl.
8 and 9.   Own answers.
10. Answers may vary – weather, location, activities, company, good planning, good health and many others.

17 **Flat Stanley**

Question types: 4 literal, 1 inferential, 1 evaluative, 4 deductive
1. The name of the book was *Flat Stanley*. The author was Jeff Brown.
2. A bulletin board fell on Stanley and made him flat.
3. He went to California for his holiday.
4. His best adventure was when he helped to capture a gang of art thieves.
5. Answers may vary – Mrs Lambchop is probably Stanley's mother.
6. The thieves would have thought he was a picture because he was flat. To look like a painting he would have needed to have kept very still.
7. Answers may vary – funny books, adventure books and fantasy stories are possibilities.
8. Answers may vary – in fact, his brother, Arthur, blows him up with a bicycle pump!
9. Answers may vary – he couldn't be squashed flat, be put in the post, flown as a kite and so on.
10. Own answer.

Instructions

 18 **How to catch a train**

Question types: 3 literal, 1 inferential, 3 evaluative, 3 deductive
1. You might buy a single ticket or a return ticket.
2. You need to hold on to your ticket in case a railway official asks to check it.
3. The three pieces of information are the time the train leaves, the platform it leaves from and the stations where the train stops.
4. It is important to stand away from the edge so that you don't risk falling under the train.
5. You can prepare to leave the train and make sure you are near the door when your station is reached.
6. You should keep clear of the doorways so that you don't get caught in the doors and don't get in the way of people entering and leaving the train.
7. You should find a secure place to stand, well away from the doors, and preferably with something to hold on to.
8. Decide if you want single or return ticket. Check you have enough money. Ask for ticket to destination. Hand over money for ticket. Wait for ticket. Move to platform to catch train.
9. Own answer.
10.   Step 8 – Wait for the train. Do not stand too near the edge of the platform. Step 15 – Step out on to the platform and move away from the edge.

19 How to grow tomatoes

Question types: 3 literal, 1 inferential, 3 evaluative, 3 deductive
1. You need tomato plants, fertiliser and water (support canes, string and space in the garden to grow the plants are also correct answers).
2. You plant the tomatoes in the garden.
3. You need to water them every day.
4. The plants would not grow very big and would have very little fruit; the plants would die.
5. The canes are needed to support the plants and to prevent them from falling over.
6. The tomatoes should be picked when they are ripe because that is when they taste best.
7. A tomato is red when it is ripe.
8. Answers may vary – sunshine is also necessary for tomatoes to grow.
9. Answers may vary – people spray tomatoes to keep insects and other pests away.
10. Sprays may contain poisons which can harm people and other creatures.

20 Catching a fish

Question types: 3 literal, 1 inferential, 1 evaluative, 5 deductive
1. Answers may vary – fishing line, hooks and landing net (a knife, weights, keepnet and bait are also correct answers).
2. The bait is fixed to the hook.
3. You put the fish in the keepnet.
4. Answers may vary – you may have to wind in any loose line to stop it getting tangled or if you can feel a fish tugging.
5. You would use a weight to allow the bait on the hook to sink down below the surface of the water.
6. Answers may vary – because the fish might snap the line or escape from the hook.
7. If you caught a very small fish it would be best to throw it back.
8. Bait is something that attracts the fish because they think they can eat it.
9. 'Cast' means to throw out the line so that it floats in the water, at a distance from where you are standing.
10. Answers may vary – it is important to be very quiet because if you make too much noise you may frighten the fish away; patience is required because you may have to wait a long time for a fish to bite.

Report

21 Sports day

Question types: 4 literal, 2 inferential, 1 evaluative, 3 deductive
1. Blue House won the trophy.
2. Ashi Khan scored the most points.
3. The champion boy athlete was Fergus Thomas.
4. Yellow House won the egg-and-spoon race and had the most fun.
5. Answers may vary – they probably did not take the day as seriously; they enjoyed winning the novelty races and didn't mind losing overall.
6. Nearly everyone in the school was there, and all the Houses tried hard to win the trophy.
7. Own answer.
8. Answers may vary – Blue House won, Ashi Khan was top girl, Fergus Thomas was top boy, Yellow House won the egg-and-spoon race and the sack race.
9. Own answer.
10. Answers may vary – to be a top athlete you would need to live a healthy life, eat and sleep well, train regularly and be determined and committed. You would also need to have natural strength, speed and talent.

22 The elephant

Question types: 4 literal, 2 inferential, 1 evaluative, 2 deductive
1. Elephants live in Africa and the south of Asia.
2. African elephants are bigger and darker in colour. They also have sloping foreheads and very large ears.
3. The elephant uses its trunk for eating, drinking and for lifting things.
4. Elephants are hunted and killed for the ivory in their tusks.
5. They might be used to move heavy loads or to carry people.
6. It is hoped elephant numbers will increase now that plastics can be used instead of ivory, and wild elephants are protected in many parts of the world. This should help elephants avoid extinction.
7. Answers may vary – ivory is used for piano keys, for ornaments and decoration of various types.
8 and 9.   Own answers.

23 The earthworm

Question types: 5 literal, 2 inferential, 1 evaluative, 2 deductive
1. The earthworm is long, round and pinkish brown in colour; it has no spine, legs or feet; it is made of rings, or segments, which are covered in hairs (also correct is that the earthworm has a blunt head).
2. Earthworms eat soil that contains decaying plant or animal matter.
3. They live underground.
4. A worm cast is the waste soil, digested by the worm, which is left in little heaps on top of the ground.
5. They enrich it with their waste, and they also loosen the soil, creating passages where air and water can enter it.
6. It would mean that the soil was fertile.
7. Answers may vary – it might become hard and infertile so that nothing would grow.
8. Own answer.
9. moist – slightly wet, damp; setae – tiny hairs; decaying – rotting
10. Answers may vary – you could keep the soil moist by watering it, loose by digging it regularly and rich by adding decaying animal and plant matter.

Explanation

24 How a rainbow is made

Question types: 2 literal, 3 inferential, 1 evaluative, 4 deductive
1. You might see a rainbow on a rainy day when the Sun is shining.
2. The drops of water split the white light up into its different colours.
3. The seven colours are red, orange, yellow, green, blue, indigo and violet.
4. White light comes from the Sun; it is the light we see.
5. You can't see a rainbow at night because there is no light.
6. Indigo and violet are shades of blue and purple.
7. Answers may vary – possibly reflected in glass, in a splash of oil mixed with water on the ground, on the skin of bubbles.
8. The child's drawing of a rainbow is required for this answer.
9. Answers may vary – for example, clouds gathering and becoming darker and animals taking shelter may indicate an approaching storm.
10. Own answer.

25 How we digest our food

Question types: 4 literal, 1 inferential, 2 evaluative, 3 deductive
1. When food is chewed it is mixed with saliva.
2. The chewed food goes into the stomach.

3. Bile comes from the liver.

4. Nutrients are building blocks of the body.

5. No, some food is left over; this is passed into the large intestine and then out of the body.

6. If you eat too much your digestive system might not be able to deal with all the extra food – this can make your stomach hurt or it can make you feel sick.

7. Answers may vary – a varied diet helps us to keep healthy by providing a full range of nutrients.

8. Answers may vary – we need foods that provide proteins, carbohydrates, fats, mineral salts and essential vitamins, such as bread, meat and fish, cheese, vegetables and fruit.

9. 'Bloodstream' means the flow of blood around a person's body.

10. It provides a picture of what the explanation tells us, and this makes it easier to follow.

26 Why an iceberg floats

Question types: 3 literal, 2 inferential, 1 evaluative, 4 deductive

1. Yes, an ice cube floats.

2. Ice is frozen water.

3. You make ice in a freezer.

4. Eight-ninths of an iceberg is submerged beneath the surface.

5. The wine would freeze, expand and push the cork out.

6. Answers may vary – the water turns into crystals of ice and expands.

7. The iceberg is compared to an ice cube. This is useful because everyone knows what an ice cube looks like.

8. false; true; true.

9. 160 metres would be below the surface of the sea; the height of the iceberg would be 180 metres.

10. Icebergs are often very big, so if a ship hit one the ship would be damaged; much of the iceberg is under water, so it is often not easy to spot.

27 Why some spiders have webs

Question types: 5 literal, 2 inferential, 2 evaluative, 1 deductive

1. It begins to build its web with a single strand of spider silk.

2. It is able to run along these strands.

3. The strands that run around the web are sticky.

4. It feels the movement made by the struggling victim.

5. It kills them and uses them as food.

6. The child's labelled diagram is required for this answer.

7. Answers may vary – this helps the reader to see that the spider's needs can be thought of as being similar to a human being's, and it helps the reader to relate more to the spider.

8. It would be a good comparison because, just like a net, the spider uses its web to catch food; also, webs and nets are similar in appearance because they are both woven.

9. true; false; false.

10. prey – the victim, the creature that is caught; pantry – a place to store food.

Argument

28 A varied diet is best

Question types: 3 literal, 3 inferential, 3 evaluative, 1 deductive

1. They make the body grow.

2. Answers may vary – meat, fish, nuts, eggs and cheese are all rich in proteins.

3. We need to eat foods that contain vitamins and minerals to keep us fit and well.

4. No one food can supply all the things we need.

5. Yes, it would provide most things needed to keep the body healthy.
6. No, it is not healthy and contains too much fat and sugar.
7. You need to eat all kinds of food to have a balanced diet; own answer for the second part of the question.
8. Own answer.
9. Answers may vary – fresh fruit would be a healthy snack.
10. Answers may vary – people like the taste of the food even though they know that it is not good for them; convenience foods and junk foods are quicker and easier to prepare; people don't always understand about healthy eating.

 ### 29 Team games are more fun

Question types: 3 literal, 2 inferential, 1 evaluative, 3 deductive
1. Answers may vary – the writer thinks that team games are better than games you play yourself (you can play them with your friends, people have to co-operate as a team and they are good fun).
2. The players have to work together if they wish to win a team game.
3. Team games help people learn how to be part of a team and are also good fun (winning can be seen as a bonus).
4. Answers may vary – you have to think of others, share the play, give players who are weaker a fair chance.
5. Answers may vary – you feel proud, pleased, happy to have contributed to the team effort.
6. Answers may vary – playing team games would help you to make friends because you would get to know people with common interests, learn to work with them and consider their needs, and you would be able to have a lot of fun with the group.
7 and 8.   Own answers.
9. develops character – strengthens your sense of self and develops you as a person; team spirit – a spirit of friendship and achievement, the feeling you get from working and playing together as a team.

 ### 30 Cats make good pets

Question types: 3 literal, 1 inferential, 4 evaluative, 2 deductive
1. Cats make good pets because they are clean, easy to feed and like to be stroked and cuddled (they are also 'beautiful' in appearance).
2. Cats scratch and spit when they are angry, they aren't able to protect the house and do not come when they are called (you cannot take them for walks, they do not travel well and they kill small birds and animals are also correct answers).
3. They scratch and spit.
4. They purr.
5–10. Own answers.

Read this poem →

THIRTY-TWO LENGTHS

One Tuesday when I was about ten
I swam thirty-two lengths
which is one mile.
And when I climbed out of the water
I felt like a big, fat lump of jelly
and my legs were like rubber
and there was this huge man there
with tremendous muscles all over him
and I went up to him and said,
"I've just swum a mile."
And he said,
"How many lengths was that then?"
"Thirty-two," I said.
And the man looked into the water and said,
"I've got a lad here who can do ninety."

Michael Rosen

Re-read the poem →

Answer the following questions.
(Use the back of the sheet for questions 4 to 10.)

1. How old was the boy when he swam a mile? _____

_____

2. On which day did he swim a mile? _____

3. How many lengths would half a mile be? _____

_____

4. Why did the boy tell the man about swimming a mile?
5. What made the boy feel like a lump of jelly?
6. How can you tell the man was very big?
7. How do you think the boy felt after talking to the man?
8. Did the man think the boy had done well?
9. Why do you think the man was proud of the boy who could do ninety lengths?
10. What sort of swimmer would be able to swim thirty-two lengths?

Read this poem →

CINDERELLA

I guess you think you know this story.
You don't. The real one's much more gory.
The phoney one, the one you know,
Was cooked up years and years ago,
And made to sound all soft and sappy
Just to keep the children happy.
Mind you, they got the first bit right,
The bit where, in the dead of night,
The Ugly Sisters, jewels and all,
Departed for the Palace Ball,
While darling little Cinderella
Was locked up in a slimy cellar,
Where rats who wanted things to eat,
Began to nibble at her feet.
She bellowed "Help!" and "Let me out!"
The Magic Fairy heard her shout.
Appearing in a blaze of light,
She said, "My dear, are you all right?"
"All right?" cried Cindy. "Can't you see
"I feel as rotten as can be!"
She beat her fist against the wall,
And shouted, "Get me to the Ball!
"There is a Disco at the Palace!
"The rest have gone and I am jalous!
"I want a dress! I want a coach!
"And earrings and a diamond brooch!
"And silver slippers, two of those!
"And lovely nylon panty-hose!
"Done up like that I'll guarantee
"The handsome Prince will fall for me!"
The Fairy said, "Hang on a tick."
She gave her wand a mighty flick
And quickly, in no time at all,
Cindy was at the Palace Ball!
It made the Ugly Sisters wince
To see her dancing with the Prince.
She held him very tight and pressed
herself against his manly chest.
The Prince himself was turned to pulp,
All he could do was gasp and gulp.

Roald Dahl

Continued on P93 →

Re-read the poem → **Answer the following questions.**

1. Where was Cinderella? _____

2. Where had the Ugly Sisters gone? _____

3. What were the rats doing? _____

_____

4. Who was the Magic Fairy in the old story of Cinderella? _____

_____

5. Why is the word **jalous** used? What should it be? _____

_____

6. Did Cindy go to the Palace in a coach? _____

7. Why did the Ugly Sisters wince when they saw Cindy dancing with the Prince? _____

_____

_____

8. Why did Cindy want to dress up? _____

_____

9. Why could the Prince only gasp and gulp? _____

_____

10. What sort of person do you think Cindy is in this story? _____

_____

_____

11. What is different about this version of Cinderella? _____

_____

_____

12. Were the Ugly Sisters fair to Cindy? _____

_____

Continued from P92 →

Read this poem

GRAMMAR

The teacher said:
A noun is a naming word.
What is the naming word in the sentence:
'He named the ship Lusitania'?
'Named,' said George.
Wrong, it's 'ship'.
Oh, said George.

The teacher said:
A verb is a doing word.
What is the doing word in the sentence:
'I like doing homework'?
'Doing,' said George.
Wrong, it's 'like'.
Oh, said George.

The teacher said:
An adjective is a describing word.
What is the describing word in the sentence:
'Describing sunsets is boring'?
'Describing,' said George.
Wrong, it's 'boring'.
I know it is, said George.

Michael Rosen

Re-read the poem

Answer the following questions.
(Use the back of the sheet for questions 6 to 10.)

1. Who is the teacher talking to? _____

2. What is a noun? _____

3. What is a verb? _____

4. Would the word **enormous** be a verb, a noun or an adjective? _____

_____

5. Is George enjoying the lesson? _____

_____

6. Why does George get all the answers wrong?
7. Do you think the teacher is good at teaching grammar?
8. Why is a noun called a naming word?
9. How many words can you think of to describe a sunset?
10. What do you like or not like about this poem?

Read this story →

THE STORY OF GIANT KIPPERNOSE

Once there was a giant called Kippernose. He lived on a lonely farm in the mountains. He was not fierce. Indeed he was as kind and as gentle as a giant could be. He liked children, and was fond of animals. He was good at telling stories. His favourite foods were ice cream, cakes, lollipops and sausages. He would help anyone, large or small. And yet he had no friends. When he went to the town to do his shopping, everyone ran away from him. Busy streets emptied in a trice. Everyone ran home, bolted their doors and closed all their windows, even on hot summer days.

Kippernose shouted, "Don't run away! I'll not hurt you! Please don't run away, I like little people. I've only come to do my shopping. Please come out. I'll tell you a good story about a dragon and a mermaid."

But it was no use. The town stayed silent and empty; the doors and windows stayed firmly closed. Poor Kippernose wanted so much to have someone to talk to. He felt so lonely that he often sat down in the town square and cried his heart out. You would think someone would take pity on him, but no one ever did. He simply couldn't understand it. He even tried going to another town, far across the mountains, but just the same thing happened.

"Has all the world gone mad?" said Kippernose to himself, and took his solitary way home.

The truth was that the people were not afraid of Kippernose, and they had not gone mad either. The truth was… that Kippernose had not had a single bath in a hundred years, or more!

John Cunliffe

Re-read the story →

Answer the following questions.
(Use the back of the sheet for questions 4 to 10.)

1. What was the giant called? _____

2. What were his favourite foods? _____

_____

3. Why did the giant want someone to talk to? _____

_____

4. Do you think all giants are like Kippernose?
5. What did the giant think would please the people?
6. What would happen if someone didn't have a bath for a hundred years or more?
7. Why wouldn't anyone take pity on the giant?
8. Does **in a trice** mean quickly or slowly?
9. What did Kippernose think made the people run away?
10. Do you think someone should tell Kippernose what is wrong?

Read this story ➡

CAM JANSEN AND THE MYSTERY OF THE UFO

Cam put her books and lunch box down. "It's cold," she said.

Cam fastened the top button of her coat. She pulled down the knitted cap she was wearing until it covered the tops of her ears.

"And it's getting dark," Eric said. "I'm not going to find anything to photograph now. Let's go home."

Eric put the camera back in its case. "I'm never around when anything happens," he complained. "And I'll bet if I am around, either I won't have my camera or I'll have run out of film."

"Or," Cam said, "you'll forget to take the lens cap off!"

Cam and Eric often spent time together. They were in the same class at school and lived next door to each other.

"If it wasn't for your hair," Cam's mother often teased, "I'd think you and Eric were twins."

Cam had what people called bright red hair, even though it was more orange than red. Eric's hair was dark brown.

Cam and Eric started walking home. They walked past a row of small shops at the edge of a shopping mall. Then they stopped at the corner and waited for the traffic lights to change.

Meow.

Cam and Eric looked up. A grey-and-white kitten was high up in a tree. The branch she was standing on was shaking. The kitten took a step towards the end of the branch. The branch shook even more.

Meow.

"I think she wants to come down," Eric said, "but she doesn't know how to."

Cam opened her lunch box. "I have a bit of tuna fish sandwich in here. Maybe I can get the kitten to come down."

Cam reached up and put a piece of tuna fish on the part of the branch closest to the trunk. The kitten saw the food and turned round carefully. The branch shook, but the kitten didn't fall. She walked down the branch and ate the tuna fish. Cam reached out for the kitten.

Eric was holding his camera. "Smile," he said, and he took a picture just as the kitten jumped into Cam's arms.

"I'll call the picture 'Local Girl Saves Untamed Feline'."

David A Adler

Continued on ▶ P97

Re-read the story **Answer the following questions.**

Comprehension Ages 9–10

1. What time of day was it? _____

2. What was Eric wanting to do? _____

_____

3. What did Cam and Eric see high up in a tree? _____

_____

4. What did Cam put on the branch? _____

_____

5. Do you think Cam is the girl's real name? _____

_____

6. Why did Cam think that tuna fish would get the kitten down? _____

_____

7. How do you think the kitten came to be in the tree? _____

_____

_____

8. Why didn't the kitten fall when the branch shook? _____

_____

_____

9. What do you think Eric will do with his picture? _____

_____

_____

10. Why couldn't Cam and Eric be twins? _____

_____

_____

_____

Continued from P96

Read this story ➡

DREAMS

The Big Friendly Giant was seated at the great table in his cave and he was doing his homework.

Sophie sat cross-legged on the table-top near by, watching him at work.

The glass jar containing the one and only good dream they had caught that day stood between them.

The BFG, with great care and patience, was printing something on a piece of paper with an enormous pencil.

"What are you writing?" Sophie asked him.

"Every dream is having its special label on the bottle," the BFG said. "How else could I be finding the one I am wanting in a hurry?"

"But can you really and truly tell what sort of a dream it's going to be simply by listening to it?" Sophie asked.

"I can," the BFG said, not looking up.

"But how? Is it by the way it hums and buzzes?"

"You is less or more right," the BFG said. "Every dream in the world is making a different sort of buzzy-hum music. And these grand swashboggling ears of mine is able to read that music."

"By music, do you mean tunes?"

"I is not meaning tunes."

"Then what do you mean?"

"Human beans is having their own music, right or left?"

"Right," Sophie said. "Lots of music."

"And sometimes human beans is very overcome when they is hearing wonderous music. They is getting shivers down their spindels. Right or left?"

"Right," Sophie said.

"So the music is saying something to them. It is sending a message. I do not think the human beans is knowing what that message is, but they is loving it just the same."

"That's about right," Sophie said.

"But because of these jumpsquiffling ears of mine," the BFG said, "I is not only able to hear the music that dreams are making but I is understanding it also."

"What do you mean understanding it?" Sophie said.

"I can read it," the BFG said. "It talks to me. It is like a langwitch."

"I find that just a little hard to believe," Sophie said.

"I'll bet you is also finding it hard to believe in quogwinkles," the BFG said, "and how they is visiting us from the stars."

"Of course I don't believe that," Sophie said.

The BFG regarded her gravely with those huge eyes of his. "I hope you will forgive me," he said, "if I tell you that human beans is thinking they is very clever, but they is not. They is nearly all of them notmuchers and squeakpips."

Roald Dahl

Continued on ▶P99

Re-read the story ➤   **Answer the following questions.**

1. What was the Big Friendly Giant doing? _____

_____

2. Who was watching him at work? _____

_____

3. What was in the glass jar? _____

4. What does the BFG collect? _____

5. Do you think Sophie is afraid of the Giant? _____

_____

6. What are **human beans**? _____

7. What is special about the Giant's ears? _____

_____

8. What does the Giant think of humans? _____

_____

9. Do you think the Giant speaks good English? Give some examples. _____

_____

_____

_____

10. What do you think a **spindel** is? _____

_____

11. Is the Giant good at keeping things in order? _____

_____

12. What do you think the Giant will do with all the dreams he collects? _____

_____

_____

Continued from P98 ➤

SCHOLASTIC **Photocopiable**

Read this story ➡

THE CAVE

He'd never seen anything like the collection of bits and pieces, odds and ends, bric-à-brac and old brock, that this Stig creature had lying about his den. There were stones and bones, fossils and bottles, skins and tins, stacks of sticks and hanks of string. There were motor-car tyres and hats from old scarecrows, nuts and bolts and bobbles from brass bedsteads. There was a coal scuttle full of dead electric light bulbs and a basin with rusty screws and nails in it. There was a pile of bracken and newspapers that looked as if it were used for a bed. The place looked as if it had never been given a tidy-up.

"I wish I lived here," said Barney.

Stig seemed to understand that Barney was approving of his home and his face lit up. He took on the air of a householder showing a visitor round his property, and began pointing out some of the things he seemed particularly proud of.

First, the plumbing. Where the water dripped through a crack in the roof of the cave he had wedged the mud-guard of a bicycle. The water ran along this, through the tube of a vacuum-cleaner, and into a big can with writing on it. By the side of this was a plastic football carefully cut in half, and Stig dipped up some water and offered it to Barney. Barney had swallowed a mouthful before he made out the writing on the can: it said WEEDKILLER. However, the water only tasted of rust and rubber.

It was dark in the back of the cave. Stig went to the front where the ashes of a fire were smoking faintly, blew on them, picked up a book that lay beside his bed, tore out a page and rolled it up, lit it at the fire, and carried it to a lamp set in a niche in the wall. As it flared up Barney could see it was in fact an old teapot, filled with some kind of oil, and with a bootlace hanging out of it for a wick.

Clive King

Continued on P101 ➡

📖 S C H O L A S T I C Photocopiable

Re-read the story **Answer the following questions.**

1. Who was looking round the den? _____

2. Who did the den belong to? _____

3. What was the bed made of? _____

_____

4. Why did Barney wish he lived there? _____

_____

5. Why did Stig's face light up? _____

_____

6. Does Stig rely on the rain for water? _____

_____

7. How do you think Stig cooked his food? _____

_____

8. What does Stig use his book for? _____

_____

9. Why was the fire at the front of the cave? _____

_____

10. Do you think Stig has lived in his den for a long time? _____

_____

_____

11. How did Stig feel about his den? _____

_____

_____

12. What do you think Barney's house is like? _____

_____

_____

Continued from P100

SCHOLASTIC Photocopiable

Read this story →

HARRY'S MAD

One immediate benefit to Harry was in the matter of homework. It did not take him long to realise that it was a much pleasanter business with Madison around.

One evening the parrot had flown upstairs to find the boy chewing his pencil and staring at an empty page.

"I'm stuck, Mad," Harry said.

Madison hopped on to Harry's shoulder and peered down at the open book.

"What have we here?" he said.

"English."

"English!" cried Madison in ringing tones. "The flower of languages, the noblest speech of all, the mother tongue that Shakespeare spake!"

"Spake?"

"Spake. Whatta we gotta do?"

"It's parts of speech," Harry said. "You've got to say which word's a noun and all that. In these sentences. Like this one – 'John fell off the wall and broke his left leg.'"

"Tough on John," said Madison, "but not difficult to answer. Here's what you've got: proper noun; – verb; – preposition; – definite article; – noun; – conjunction; – verb; – pronoun; – adjective; – noun. Get it?"

"No," said Harry.

But by the time that Madison had explained it and dictated it with the words all correctly spelled, Harry had learned quite a lot.

"You've got these all right, Harry," his teacher said next day in a puzzled voice. "Your dad help you?"

"No," said Harry. "A little bird told me."

Dick King-Smith

Re-read the story →

Answer the following questions.
(Use the back of the sheet for questions 3 to 10.)

1. What is the name of the parrot? _____

2. Why was Harry chewing his pencil? _____

_____

3. What subject had Harry got for homework?
4. Why couldn't Harry do his homework?
5. Which room do you think Harry did his homework in?
6. How can you tell Madison is good at English?
7. Did the parrot help Harry to understand what he was doing?
8. Why was Harry's teacher puzzled?
9. Do you think Harry is good at English?
10. How much help is the parrot to Harry?

Read this play

THE STRANGE CREATURE

SCENE 1

A lady is talking to a reporter at the office of the Daily Bugle. She is very upset.

LADY: It was huge, I tell you, and making a loud hissing noise. It was staring at me with its wild eyes!

REPORTER: Now calm down, Madam. Tell me exactly what happened.

LADY: Well, I was walking by Poddle Wood with Ralph – he's my dog – when it stuck its head out over the tops of the bushes!

REPORTER: What stuck its head out?

LADY: This awful creature! I thought I would die of fright!

REPORTER: Can you describe it, Madam?

LADY: Well, it was huge, like I said. About as big as a double-decker bus. It was making a horrible, hissing noise and rustling. I am sure it was getting ready to attack me! You'd better come and see!

SCENE 2

At the edge of Poddle Wood.

LADY: Yes, this is the place – I recognise the bushes. (A *man in flying kit is suddenly seen staggering out of the bushes*.) Oh look! Who is that man? And what has happened to the creature?

REPORTER: Hey, sir! Have you seen a huge, hissing creature in the bushes?

MAN: That was my hot-air balloon. I came down in the wood by accident and my balloon tore on the trees as it fell through. Where am I?

LADY: You'd better come with me, young man, you could do with a cup of tea.

REPORTER: Hang on! I'll just get a picture for my paper.

Re-read the play

Answer the following questions on the back of the sheet.

1. Who is the lady talking to at the *Daily Bugle*?
2. Where had she been walking?
3. Why was the lady so upset?
4. Do you think Poddle Wood is a long way from the *Daily Bugle* office?
5. Do you think the reporter believed the lady's story?
6. What was the hissing noise the lady heard?
7. Why do you think the balloon came down in the wood?
8. Why did the lady think the man needed a cup of tea?
9. Why did the lady go to the *Daily Bugle*?
10. Describe what you think the balloon looked like when it was flying.

Read this play →

THE RESCUE

SCENE 1

A boy and girl are sitting on a grassy canal bank with their fishing nets and jam jars. A canal boat is coming down the canal in the distance.

JACK: There don't seem to be many fish about today. How are you doing?

TINA: I've only got one little one. I don't know what it is.

JACK: Let's have a look – well, it's got spikes on its back so I think it is a stickleback. Hey! Look at that canal boat coming. I wonder why that lady is waving her arms about?

TINA: Never mind the boat! What's this floating along? Oh! It's a little dog! Can we get it to the side with our fishing nets?

(The children manage to get the dog to the side and lift it out.)

TINA: It's only a puppy – poor little thing!

JACK: It must belong to that lady on the boat.

SCENE 2

The children are aboard the boat having lemonade and biscuits. The lady is fussing over her dog.

LADY: How clever of you to save little Toby! He fell off the boat when it bumped into the lock gate. I was so afraid he would drown.

TINA: Mum made Jack and me have swimming lessons when we came to live near the canal. She wouldn't let us come fishing till we could swim. But little Toby can swim without any lessons!

LADY: Is that your house by the bridge? We'll tie up here and I'll ask your mum if you can come to the next lock with us as a thank you for saving Toby.

SCENE 3

Tina and Jack are aboard the canal boat sitting on the deck with Toby. The boat is approaching a lock.

JACK: Heave to! The lock gate is just ahead!

LADY: Stop the engine, Fred! Well! That's a bit of luck! The lock is full of water so we can go straight in when we've opened the gates.

(Fred and the lady jump ashore and open the gates.)

FRED: Okay! All aboard! Let's get the boat into the lock and close the gates again.

(Fred and the lady get the boat into the lock and close the gates.)

LADY: Open the sluices, Fred! We'll have to wait now for the water to go down, so that we can go through the other gates.

TINA: This is fun! We are going down. It's like being in a very slow lift!

JACK: We must be low enough now.

FRED: Open the gates, Fred!

(Fred opens the gates and the boat glides through.)

LADY: Here you are children, this is where you get off!

TINA AND JACK: Thank you for the ride, it's been really good!

Continued on ▶ P105

Re-read the play ▶   **Answer the following questions.**

1. What are Jack and Tina doing by the canal? _____

_____

2. What sort of fish has Tina caught? _____

_____

3. Why was the lady waving her arms about? _____

_____

4. How did Toby come to be in the water? _____

_____

5. Why did the lady go to the children's mum? _____

_____

6. Why wouldn't the children's mum let them go fishing before they could swim? _____

_____

7. Have the children always lived near the canal? _____

_____

8. How do you think the lady felt when her dog was saved? _____

_____

9. Why did the lady ask Fred to stop the engine? _____

_____

10. Why was it lucky that the lock was full of water? _____

_____

11. Why did Fred have to open the sluices? _____

_____

12. What would be good about a trip on a canal boat? _____

_____

Continued from ▶ P104

Read this recount →

THE BEATLES

The Beatles were a pop group whose fame swept the world in the 1960s. 'Beatlemania' broke out wherever The Beatles went. Teenage girls would fight in the streets for seats at their concerts. During the concerts they screamed for joy, or fainted because the heat and excitement were too much for them!

Some tried to scramble onto the stage to get as near to the four young men as they possibly could. There were often guards to hold the girls back, but when a concert came to an end they were hard to control. Girls surged to the front for a final chance to snatch at The Beatles' hair or clothes.

The Beatles grew very rich as thousands of copies of their records were sold every day. One had the title 'A Hard Day's Night'. This summed up what The Beatles' lives were like. Often, they spent a hard day getting microphones ready and practising songs. Then at night came the time that mattered most – the concert, the getaway in a flashy car and finally sleep in a posh hotel.

The Beatles were not used to wealth and comfort. They had grown up during the 1940s in rather rough parts of Liverpool, when food and other things were scarce. This was because the Second World War was raging when they were very young. For years the boys never met at all. They went to school in different parts of the city; but although they were taught music, they had to learn for themselves that playing drums and guitars is fun. Richards Starkey's bedroom was full of drums. The other boys played guitars and sang. By the time they were 20 their music-making had brought them together. Starkey had already changed his name to Ringo Starr – it sounded better, and it went with all the rings he wore. They all agreed that The Beatles would be a good name for the group. Their music would certainly have lots of beat!

The years of Beatlemania came to a sudden end when The Beatles quarrelled. The group split up in 1971; but all four Beatles have made records separately since then, while Ringo Starr has also appeared in several films.

Tony T Triggs

Continued on ▶P107

Re-read the recount   **Answer the following questions.**

1. How many young men were in The Beatles group? _____

2. What was Ringo Starr really called? _____

3. When did The Beatles' fame sweep the world? _____

_____

4. Why did the girls get so excited at the concerts? _____

_____

5. What was the boys' life like when they were very young? _____

_____

6. Why didn't the boys meet until they were about 20 years old? _____

_____

7. How did The Beatles get so rich? _____

_____

8. Do you think 'The Beatles' was a good name for them? _____

_____

_____

9. Had the boys always liked music? _____

_____

10. What kind of place is a **posh hotel**? _____

_____

11. Did the boys have to work hard for their fame? _____

_____

12. Why did the girls want to snatch at The Beatles' hair and clothes? _____

_____

Continued from P106

Read this recount →

SWIMMING LESSONS

We live by a canal. My friends and I love going there. Sometimes we try catching fish and sometimes we throw stones at bits of wood that are floating in the water. My mum was very worried about me falling in and drowning because I couldn't swim so she made me go to swimming lessons.

I didn't really like going much at first. The water was quite cold at the swimming pool and I didn't like getting my face wet. I'm used to it now and it's good fun. There are 12 boys and girls in my class. We all started off wearing armbands and, after having a go at doggy paddle, our teacher taught us how to do the breaststroke. It was quite difficult to begin with, trying to make our arms and legs work properly together. Luckily our armbands stopped us from sinking!

I went to swimming every week on Saturday morning. I made friends with another boy in the class. He's good at swimming – our teacher says he's a 'natural'. After a few lessons, we had to try swimming without our armbands. My friend could do it easily and swam a whole width. I kept sinking at first and I got really fed up. Then all of a sudden, I could do it! I was able to swim! I shall never forget the day I first swam a length! I was given my 25-metre badge. My mum has sewn the badge on my swimming trunks – it looks good! My mum says she is very proud of me and she doesn't mind me going down to the canal now.

Re-read the recount →

Answer the following questions.
(Use the back of the sheet for questions 4 to 10.)

1. Where does the writer live? _____

2. Why did the writer have to learn to swim? _____

_____

3. What makes a canal a dangerous place? _____

_____

_____

4. Why did the writer like going to the canal?
5. Why was learning the breaststroke difficult?
6. Why did the swimming teacher call the writer's friend a **'natural'**?
7. How many metres long is the swimming pool?
8. How do you think the writer felt after first swimming a length?
9. Is the writer a boy or a girl?
10. Could any of the children swim before they had swimming lessons?

Read these instructions

BATTLESHIPS

This is a game for two players. All you need are four pieces of squared paper and a pencil. Each player has two pieces of paper. On each piece of paper label twelve squares along the top, A to L, and twelve squares down the side, 1 to 12. These pieces of paper represent the ocean.

On one of their pieces of paper, both players mark out six ships each on their grid, for example one battleship, two destroyers and three submarines. Five squares can be used for a battleship, three squares for a destroyer and two squares for a submarine. The fleet can be arranged anywhere on the ocean – just make sure your opponent can't see where your ships are!

The second piece of paper is used as a spare grid to record a player's 'shots'. One player starts the game by firing the first shot (saying, for example, 'I am firing at H8'), naming a square that might be occupied by a ship in his opponent's fleet. He then marks down the shot he made on his spare piece of paper so that he doesn't aim at that square again and waste a shot.

The other player then has to tell him whether he has made a 'hit', and crosses off the square if a 'hit' has been made. He does not need to tell his opponent which of his ships has been damaged. Then the second player has a turn to fire his 'gun' in the same way. The game continues with each player taking it in turns to have a 'shot'.

A ship is 'sunk' when each square of the ship has been hit by the other player. The winner is the first player to sink the whole of his opponent's fleet.

Re-read the instructions

Answer the following questions.
(Use the back of the sheet for questions 4 to 10.)

1. How many players does the game need? _____

2. What sort of paper do you need? _____

_____

3. What other ships could you have in your fleet? _____

_____

4. What are the letters and numbers for?
5. When might you play this game?
6. What could you do if you didn't have any squared paper?
7. Is this an easy game to play?
8. Could more than two people play the game at a time?
9. What changes to the rules could you have to make the game quicker?
10. What skills do you need to play the game successfully?

Read these instructions

MAKING AN AQUARIUM

You will need:
a straight-sided glass tank
rounded pebbles or gravel
three or four larger stones
rainwater or pond water
pond weed from a shop or pond

What to do:
1. First, carefully wash and dry the glass tank. Wash the pebbles or gravel. Scrub the stones well to remove any soil or dirt.
2. Collect some rain or pond water in a clean bucket. Do not use tap water.
3. Put a layer of pebbles, gravel or a mixture of both in the bottom of the tank. (A layer of about 3cm would be about right.) The layer does not need to be completely level. It could slope a little down to the front of the tank. This makes it easier to remove any uneaten pieces of food. Arrange the larger stones to look natural, as if they were in a pond or stream.
4. Gently fill the tank three-quarters full with the rainwater or pond water using a jug.
5. Put in the pond weed. This is usually strands of Canadian pond weed. You can trap the ends of the strands under the larger stones. The pond weed puts oxygen into the water and aerates it.
6. Leave the tank for a day to settle, and for the water to come up to room temperature.
7. Stock the aquarium with three or four water snails. They will keep the tank clean by removing any rubbish on the bottom of the tank and by eating the green algae that grows on the glass sides.
8. Put in two or three goldfish. Make sure the water in which you brought them home from the shop is at the same temperature as the water in the tank.
9. Place the aquarium in a cool, shady place.
10. Feed the fish once or twice a week with a pinch of fish food or tiny amounts of uncooked porridge oats.

Continued on P111

Re-read the instructions **Answer the following questions.**

1. What sort of tank will you need? _____

_____

2. What kind of water should you use? _____

_____

3. Why is it best not to use tap water? _____

_____

4. Where could you get water snails from? _____

_____

5. Why do you need water snails in the aquarium? _____

_____

6. Why should the tank be in a cool, shady place? _____

_____

7. How does pond weed aerate the water? _____

_____

8. How else could you make the aquarium look attractive? _____

_____

_____

9. Why does the water in which you brought the goldfish home need to be at the same temperature as the water in the aquarium?

_____

_____

_____

10. How often will you need to change the water in the aquarium? _____

_____

_____

Continued from P110

Read these instructions ➤

HOW TO FIND INFORMATION IN A BOOK

Information books are non-fiction and contain facts about different subjects. They are all grouped together in the public library or school library. Information books have a number on their spines. This number tells you what subject group each book is in. The books are put on the shelves in numerical order so that you can find the one you want quickly.

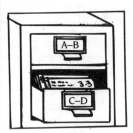

When you want to find information, first find out what number the subject you need will have by looking it up in a subject catalogue. Look through the books in the library with this number and read the titles. The titles will give you a hint of what the books are about. Choose the book you think will have the information you need.

Look at the contents page at the beginning of the book and read the chapter headings to see if your subject is included. If it is, make a list of 'key words' for your subject and look for these in the index at the back of the book to see if any of your key words are listed. If they are, make a note of the page numbers where the information can be found.

Skim through the book to see if there are any illustrations, charts or diagrams that may be useful for your work.

If you are satisfied that the book has the information you need, start your work by looking on the pages you found in the chapter headings or index. Read through the information and make notes about what you have found out.

When you have made all the notes you need, write your piece of work in your own words using your notes to help you.

Continued on P113 ➤

Re-read the instructions

Answer the following questions.

1. What do information books have on their spines in the school or public library? _____

_____

2. How will you find the number for the subject you need? _____

_____

3. How could the title of a book give a hint of what the book is about? _____

_____

4. What are **'key words'**? _____

_____

5. What would be three key words for information about how to look after a dog? _____

_____

6. How is the index of the book useful? _____

_____

7. Is a library a good place to go for information? _____

_____

8. What skills do you need to be able to use information books? _____

_____

_____

_____

9. Will you find made-up adventure stories in the non-fiction section? _____

_____

_____

10. Where will you find out what the chapters are called in the book? _____

_____

_____

Continued from P112

Read this report

THE ASHTON CRICKET CLUB

The cricket club has had quite a good year. The club has won more away matches than last year and all but one of the home matches.

The First XI finished the season in fourth place in the Sunday League, Division Two. This was a good effort. Seven games were won, six lost and five games were rained off. Tom Kipper scored a maiden century in a match against Bigton and Ted Potter scored 109 not out when the team played at home against Stockbury.

The Second XI played twelve games. They won six and lost six. They were luckier with the weather than the First XI. Two of the batsmen had outstanding seasons. Bob Flick scored a total of 467 runs including two centuries. Jack Hobble scored a total of 455 runs, again including two centuries. Jack has made a remarkable recovery from breaking his leg at the Christmas party.

The Ashton junior team had a successful season. There are some promising batsmen and bowlers in the team. Michelle Carter made a very good wicket keeper and had several good catches. The three other girls on the team scored most of the runs for the season. Four members of the junior team, two boys and two girls, will attend the cricket coaching course at the Indoor Cricket Centre in November. This will improve the level of coaching for the juniors. New members for the junior team would be welcome.

Mr Sparrow, the club's umpire, retired at the end of the season. He has umpired the matches for 43 years and it was only his failing eyesight that forced him to retire. He was made a life member of the club at his retirement party, and presented with a pair of binoculars. Mr Sparrow presented a set of new wickets to the club.

Mr Leather, Mayor of Ashton and keen supporter, has given the cricket club a new silver cup for the most promising junior. A presentation evening will be held in the cricket club on Saturday 15 November. The prizes will be presented by the president of the club, Mr Legg. The catering committee will provide the food and the Cricketer's Arms will provide the licensed bar. Tickets are £13.50 each (£7.50 for juniors) from Mrs Hall, the cricket club secretary.

Continued on P115

Re-read the report ➤ **Answer the following questions.**

1. What was the name of the cricket club? _____

2. Who was the president of the club? _____

3. How many teams did the club have? _____

_____

4. What is an **away** match? _____

_____

5. How many runs did Tom Kipper score against Bigton? _____

_____

6. How will the coaching course help the junior team? _____

_____

_____

7. Why did Mr Sparrow's eyesight force him to retire? _____

_____

8. On which day of the week were the matches played? _____

_____

9. How many runs are there in a century? _____

_____

10. Who do you think will get the cup for the most promising junior? _____

_____

11. What skills do you need to be good at cricket? _____

_____

_____

12. Who enjoys cricket matches the most, the players or the people watching? _____

_____

Continued from P114 ➤

Read this report

THE GARDEN PRODUCE SHOW

The local Garden Produce Show was held on 11 August and it was a great success as usual. The hall was a blaze of colour and there was a record number of entries. The high standard of the produce made the judging very difficult.

The show was held for the first time in the new community centre that was opened earlier in the year. There were classes for every kind of fruit, flower and vegetable as well as classes for children to enter with their vegetable animals and miniature gardens. The tasty tomato growing and cake-making classes introduced last year proved popular once more.

Mr Cooper won first prize again for his enormous onion grown from seed. It weighed a record 3.5 kilograms. The first prize for the longest runner bean had to be shared between Mrs Green and her next-door neighbour, Mr Todd. Mrs Green thought the prize should have been hers. She was surprised to learn that Mr Todd had grown any beans to enter, as he had never been interested in gardening.

The Dibble twins won first prize for their joint entry of a truly magnificent vegetable dragon. People were amazed that children who were only five years old could have done so well. The judge said their parents must have given them a lot of encouragement. Daisy Smith's miniature garden was the best of the class. Her miniature garden was arranged around a small thatched cottage she had made.

Mr Nutt won first prize for his excellent fruit cake, while Tommy Botter took first prize for his shortbread. Mrs Green won first prize with her apple chutney as usual.

The prizes were presented by the president of the Garden Club, Mr Plant, who congratulated all the people who entered and thanked the judges for carrying out their difficult task.

Continued on **P117**

Re-read the report

Answer the following questions.

1. Where was the Garden Produce Show held? _____

_____

2. Who won first prize for a vegetable animal? _____

_____

3. Which classes had been held for the first time the year before? _____

_____

4. Where did Mrs Green suspect Mr Todd had got his runner bean from? _____

_____

5. Write down five other vegetables that you think could have been entered. _____

_____

_____

6. Has the show been held in the community centre before? _____

_____

7. Do you think the Dibble twins made their vegetable animal all by themselves? _____

_____

_____

8. Do you think Mr Cooper expected to win a prize with his onion? _____

_____

_____

9. What do you think made the **blaze of colour**? _____

_____

_____

10. Was it a surprise to anyone that Mrs Green's chutney won first prize? _____

_____

_____

Continued from P116

Read this explanation →

THE WATER CYCLE

After it has stopped raining, the ground is soaking wet and puddles of water are left in dips and hollows on the roads and paths. Gradually, the ground dries up and the puddles disappear. The water has evaporated and has turned into water vapour. This is made up of very tiny droplets of water like those in steam but even smaller. You can't see it but the water vapour is in the air. The warmer the air, the more water vapour it can hold.

Water from the rivers and sea evaporates in the same way all the time. The water vapour in the air rises up into the sky. As the temperature of the air gets colder, the water vapour turns into tiny droplets of water again and wispy clouds are formed.

The droplets of water in the clouds join together and these drops get bigger and bigger. The clouds get thicker and bigger and turn grey. The water drops get so heavy that they start to fall as rain. In the winter if the air is very cold, the water vapour in the clouds forms ice crystals and these fall to earth as snow. Hail is formed when raindrops freeze as they fall through the air.

When the rainwater falls on the earth, it trickles through the ground and runs into the rivers, lakes and sea. Water is continually evaporating from all these places, turning into water vapour and rising up through the air to form clouds high up in the sky, only to fall again as rain. In this way, the water we have on earth just goes round and round in the water cycle.

Re-read the explanation →

Answer the following questions.
(Use the back of the sheet for questions 4 to 10.)

1. What happens to the water in the puddles left by the rain? _____

_____

2. What are the clouds made of? _____

3. Why do wet clothes dry when they are hung up outside? _____

_____

4. Why do clouds turn grey?
5. Do you think the Stone Age people could have used the same water as us?
6. How would you need to dress if the clouds were grey when you went outside?
7. How is snow formed?
8. How important do you think rain is to us?
9. Do you think the amount of water in the world has always been the same?
10. Draw a diagram to show how the water cycle works.

Read this explanation

ICE-CAPS

Ice-caps are huge areas of ice in the polar regions of the world. The polar regions are at the North and South Poles of the world. These regions are as far as they can be from the Equator, which circles the Earth (the Equator is where the Sun is at its hottest).

It is so cold at the North and South Poles that the seas there are frozen. The ice-cap at the South Pole, Antarctica, has formed over a large island of solid land. At the North Pole, the Arctic is a huge ocean that has frozen solid into one big sheet of ice floating on the top of the sea, making a vast island of ice. The ice here is only a few metres thick. The ice over the land of the Antarctic can be as much as two kilometres thick.

The climate in the Arctic is very, very cold. The temperature is always below freezing or so little above it that the ice never completely melts away. In the summer, the edges of the Arctic ice sheet slowly melt in the warmth of the Sun. Huge chunks of ice break away and float out to sea. These chunks of ice are icebergs. Some of the very big icebergs float right away into mid-ocean and they are a serious danger to ships.

If all the ice in the polar regions melted, the water from the ice would raise the level of the oceans in the world by 75 metres!

Re-read the explanation

Answer the following questions.
(Use the back of the sheet for questions 5 to 10.)

1. Where are the polar regions? _____

_____

2. What has happened to the sea at the North and South Poles? _____

_____

3. Why is it so cold in the polar regions? _____

_____

4. What causes chunks of ice to break off the ice-cap in the Arctic? _____

_____

5. What sort of clothes would you need to wear to visit the Arctic?
6. What would happen to the land of the world if all the ice at the ice-caps melted?
7. How are icebergs dangerous to ships?
8. When would be the best time to visit the North Pole?
9. What would happen if you fell into the sea at the polar regions?
10. What could an explorer use for water in the Arctic?

Read this explanation

CANAL LOCKS

Canals are man-made waterways that have been used for thousands of years. Until the 1500s, canals could only be built across flat land. When canal locks were invented, canals could be built across hills too. The locks made it possible for boats to sail over the hills by lifting them up in a series of steps from one level to another.

Locks are gates built across rivers to connect two different levels of water. Boats cannot travel up a waterfall to go from a lower to a higher stretch of river, but they can go through a lock. Locks are also used on rivers and canals to control the water level. The locks act as dams on rivers to prevent the water running too swiftly to the sea.

A lock is a small area of the waterway with gates at both ends. The sides and the bottom of the lock are made of bricks or concrete. There are sluices in the lock gates and these help to control the flow of water. A sluice is like a serving hatch which you sometimes see in the wall between a kitchen and dining room. A square is cut from the wood of the lock gate and the gap is covered by a sliding door. When the sliding door or shutter is covering the square hole in the gate, no water can get through. But when the shutter is lifted the water flows through the hole.

If a boat is going from a higher level of a canal to a lower level, the water in the lock has to be at the same level as the water in the canal at the higher level. The lock gates are opened and the boat enters the lock. The lock gates are closed behind the boat so the boat is now shut in the lock.

Now the water level in the lock has to be made the same as the lower level of the canal. To do this, the sluices are opened in the lock gates in front of the boat and the water flows out of the lock through the sluices. The water in the lock gets lower and lower until it is at the same level as the lower part of the canal. The lock gates in front of the boat are opened and the boat can go ahead out of the lock and go on its journey.

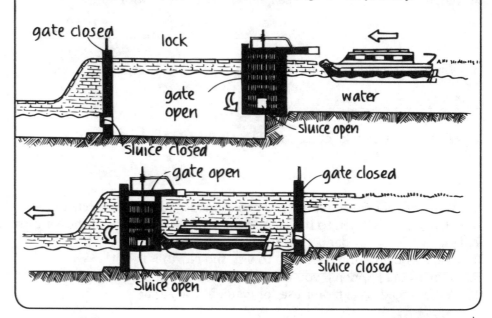

Continued on P121

Re-read the explanation

Answer the following questions.

1. When were locks invented? _____

2. What were boats able to do after locks were invented? _____
_____

3. What is the difference between a river and a canal? _____
_____

4. What is used to make the sides and the bottom of the lock? _____
_____

5. How do sluices control the flow of water? _____
_____

6. Why does a boat have to wait in a lock? _____
_____

7. How useful are canals today? _____
_____

8. What heavy cargoes do you think could be moved by the canal boats? _____
_____

9. Why do you think canals were invented? _____
_____

10. Write out the steps needed for a boat to go from a lower level of a canal to a higher level.
_____
_____
_____

11. Does water flow along a canal as it does in a river? _____
_____

12. Do you think canals are a quick way to travel? _____
_____

Continued from P120

Read this argument

HOMEWORK

Many teachers and parents think that giving children school work to do at home is a good thing. Older children at secondary school need to do homework to be able to learn enough to pass exams. There isn't enough time in the lessons to do all the things they need to know or finish off the work they have started.

If children are given homework from about the age of seven, it gets them into the habit of working at home, so that they are used to doing it by the time they go to their secondary school. Homework helps parents to understand what their children are learning at school. It gives them the chance to help their children if they need it and take an interest in what they are doing.

If the children can't do their homework because they don't understand it, the teachers will get to know this and they will be able to give them extra help. Doing school work at home helps children to learn to concentrate and work on their own. This is a great advantage when the children are older and go to college or university.

People who are against homework say children are too tired after a day at school to work at home and they need time to play. It can be difficult sometimes in a crowded house to find somewhere quiet to do the work. Other members of the family may want to watch television and younger members of the family may be noisy. Busy parents may not have time to help their children if they need it and this could cause problems. If children have to do homework, there is no time to play or watch TV before they go to bed. Some children make a fuss about doing homework and parents have a job to get them to do it, so it can all end in tears.

Re-read the argument

Answer the following questions.
(Use the back of the sheet for questions 3 to 9.)

1. Why do older children need to do school work at home? _____

_____

2. Do all teachers and parents think homework is a good thing? _____

_____

3. How does homework help parents?
4. Why could it be difficult to find a quiet place to do the homework?
5. Why would children make a fuss about doing homework?
6. What are some of the things younger children could do for homework?
7. Do you think it is a good idea to do homework?
8. Why do young children need to get into the habit of doing homework?
9. When is the best time for you to do homework?

Poetry

1 **Thirty-two lengths**

Question types: 2 literal, 2 inferential, 3 evaluative, 3 deductive
1. The boy was about ten years old.
2. He swam a mile on a Tuesday.
3. Half a mile would be sixteen lengths.
4. He told the man because he was so pleased to have swum a mile.
5. The boy was very tired.
6. The man was huge and had enormous muscles.
7–9. Own answers.
10. Answers may vary – only a strong swimmer would be able to swim thirty-two lengths, even though the boy whom the man knew could swim ninety.

2 **Cinderella**

Question types: 3 literal, 3 inferential, 3 evaluative, 3 deductive
1. Cinderella was in a cellar.
2. The Ugly Sisters had gone to the Palace Ball.
3. The rats were nibbling Cinderella's feet.
4. The Magic Fairy was the Fairy Godmother.
5. The word 'jalous' is used to rhyme with 'palace'; the word should be 'jealous'.
6. No, Cindy went to the Palace by magic.
7. They wanted to dance with the Prince themselves.
8. She wanted the Prince to notice her.
9. Cindy was holding the Prince very tightly.
10–12. Own answers.

3 **Grammar**

Question types: 3 literal, 2 inferential, 3 evaluative, 2 deductive
1. The teacher is talking to George.
2. A noun is a naming word.
3. A verb is a doing word.
4. The word 'enormous' would be an adjective.
5. Own answer.
6. George doesn't understand the lesson.
7. Own answer.
8. A noun gives objects a name.
9 and 10. Own answers.

Narrative

4 **The story of Giant Kippernose**

Question types: 2 literal, 3 inferential, 2 evaluative, 3 deductive
1. The giant was called Kippernose.
2. His favourite foods were ice cream, cakes, lollipops and sausages.
3. He was lonely.
4. Own answer.
5. He thought the people would like his stories.
6. A person would get very dirty and smelly.
7. He was too dirty to go near.
8. 'In a trice' means very quickly.
9. Kippernose thought the people were afraid of him.
10. Own answer.

5 **Cam Jansen and the mystery of the UFO**

Question types: 2 literal, 2 inferential, 2 evaluative, 4 deductive
1. It was late afternoon.
2. Eric wanted to take photographs.
3. They saw a grey and white kitten.
4. Cam put some tuna fish on the branch.
5. No, it is a shortened name.
6. Cam knew that cats like fish.
7. Own answer.
8. Cats are good at balancing.
9. Answers might vary – he might give it to a local newspaper.
10. They are not related, and their hair colour is very different; Cam has bright red hair and Eric's is dark brown.

6 **Dreams**

Question types: 3 literal, 3 inferential, 3 evaluative, 3 deductive
1. The Big Friendly Giant was doing his homework.
2. Sophie was watching the Giant.
3. There was a dream in the glass jar.
4. The BFG collects dreams.
5. Sophie and the Giant are friends so she is not afraid.
6. 'Human beans' are really human beings.
7. The Giant's ears can understand the music the dreams make.
8 and 9.   Own answers.
10. A 'spindel' is a spine in this story.
11. The Giant is good at keeping things in order because he labels the jars.
12. Own answer.

7 **The cave**

Question types: 3 literal, 3 inferential, 3 evaluative, 3 deductive
1. Barney was looking round the den.
2. The den belonged to Stig.
3. The bed was made of bracken and newspapers.
4. Barney liked the den being untidy and full of interesting things.
5. Stig was pleased that Barney liked his home.
6. Yes, the rain would be helpful, as Stig's water came through the roof of the cave.
7. Stig cooked his food on a fire.
8. He uses the pages to light his lamp.
9. The fire was at the front so the smoke could go out.
10. Own answer.
11. Answers may vary – he felt proud of his den.
12. Own answer.

8 **Harry's Mad**

Question types: 2 literal, 4 inferential, 2 evaluative, 2 deductive
1. The name of the parrot is Madison.
2. Harry couldn't do his homework.
3. Harry had English for homework.
4. He was stuck – it was difficult.
5. Answers may vary – Harry was doing his homework upstairs in his bedroom.
6. Madison can do the homework easily.
7. Eventually, the parrot did help Harry to understand.
8. Harry didn't usually get his homework right.
9 and 10. Own answers.

Drama

9 The strange creature

Question types: 2 literal, 2 inferential, 3 evaluative, 3 deductive
1. The lady is talking to a reporter.
2. She had been walking by Poddle Wood.
3. She was upset because a strange creature had frightened her.
4. Answers may vary – it is probably not very far from the *Daily Bugle* office, certainly within walking distance.
5. Own answer.
6. The hissing noise was the gas coming out of the balloon.
7. Own answer.
8. The lady thought that the man needed a cup of tea because he had had an accident.
9. She went to the *Daily Bugle* because she wanted her story to be put in the paper.
10. Own answer.

10 The rescue

Question types: 2 literal, 3 inferential, 2 evaluative, 5 deductive
1. Jack and Tina are fishing.
2. Tina has caught a stickleback.
3. The lady was trying to attract the children's attention.
4. He lost his balance when the boat bumped into the lock gate.
5. She wanted to let their mum know where they were.
6. She was afraid they might fall in the canal and drown.
7. No, the children haven't always lived there.
8. Own answer.
9. She didn't want the boat to bump into the lock gate.
10. They didn't have to wait for the lock to fill.
11. Fred had to open the sluices to let the water out of the lock.
12. Own answer.

Recount

11 The Beatles

Question types: 3 literal, 3 inferential, 3 evaluative, 3 deductive
1. There were four young men in The Beatles.
2. Ringo Starr's real name was Richard Starkey.
3. Their fame swept the world in the 1960s.
4. Answers may vary – they were excited because they were seeing the group that they liked so much.
5. Answers may vary – they were not wealthy and times were hard.
6. They went to school in different parts of Liverpool.
7. The Beatles became rich because they sold thousands of records.
8. Own answer.
9. The boys had always liked music.
10. A posh hotel is one that is usually modern, comfortable and expensive.
11. The boys had to work very hard when they gave a concert.
12. They wanted to touch them because they were seeing them in real life. They wanted to have something belonging to The Beatles.

12 **Swimming lessons**

Question types: 2 literal, 5 inferential, 2 evaluative, 1 deductive
1. The writer lives by the canal.
2. The writer's mum was worried about him drowning.
3. Own answer.
4. He liked to try to catch fish and throw stones at pieces of wood in the water.
5. It was difficult to make your arms and legs work together.
6. The boy found it easy to learn to swim.
7. The pool is 25 metres long.
8. Own answer.
9. The writer is a boy.
10. None of the children could swim when they started.

Instructions

13 **Battleships**

Question types: 2 literal, 2 inferential, 3 evaluative, 3 deductive
1. The game needs two players.
2. You need squared paper.
3. Answers may vary – you could put in an aircraft carrier, a minesweeper or a corvette.
4. The letters and numbers give the grid reference.
5. Own answer.
6. You could measure out and draw the squares yourself.
7 and 8.   Own answers.
9. Answers may vary – you could fire more than one shot at each turn.
10. You need to be able to read a grid reference.

14 **Making an aquarium**

Question types: 2 literal, 2 inferential, 1 evaluative, 5 deductive
1. You will need a straight-sided glass tank.
2. You should use rainwater or pond water.
3. Tap water has been purified with chlorine.
4. You could get water snails from a pond or a shop.
5. Water snails keep the tank clean.
6. The water might get too hot in a sunny place.
7. Oxygen from the pond weed goes into the water.
8. Own answer.
9. The water needs to be the same so that the fish don't have a sudden change of temperature.
10. You will need to change the water regularly – if the water becomes cloudy it is a sign that it should be changed.

15 **How to find information in a book**

Question types: 2 literal, 4 inferential, 2 evaluative, 2 deductive
1. Information books have a subject number on their spines.
2. The number will be in the subject catalogue.
3. The words used in a title could give a hint.
4. 'Key words' are words that can be thought of as important within a particular subject.
5. Own answer.
6. The index gives the page numbers where information can be found.
7 and 8.   Own answers.
9. Made-up stories are fiction, so they will not be in the non-fiction section.
10. The chapter headings will be in the contents list.

Report

16 The Ashton Cricket Club

Question types: 3 literal, 2 inferential, 3 evaluative, 4 deductive
1. The club was called the Ashton Cricket Club.
2. The president of the club was Mr Legg.
3. The club had three teams.
4. An away match is played at an opponent's ground.
5. Tom Kipper scored at least 100 runs.
6. A coaching course will develop their skills and improve their play.
7. He was unable to see properly what was happening in the game.
8. The matches were played on Sundays.
9. There are 100 runs in a century.
10–12. Own answers.

17 The Garden Produce Show

Question types: 2 literal, 4 inferential, 3 evaluative, 1 deductive
1. The Garden Produce Show was held in the community centre hall.
2. The Dibble twins won first prize.
3. Tomato growing and cake making classes had been held for the first time the year before.
4. Perhaps she thought he had taken the runner bean from her garden.
5. Own answer.
6. The show has not been held in the community centre before as it is new.
7 and 8.   Own answers.
9. The flowers and plants in the show would make a blaze of colour.
10. No, people expected Mrs Green to win.

Explanation

18 The water cycle

Question types: 2 literal, 4 inferential, 3 evaluative, 1 deductive
1. The water in the puddles evaporates.
2. The clouds are made of little droplets of water.
3. The water in the clothes evaporates.
4. The clouds turn grey when the water droplets join and get bigger and bigger.
5. Own answer.
6. You would need to wear rainproof clothes.
7. Snow is formed by water drops in the clouds freezing into ice crystals.
8 and 9.   Own answers.
10.

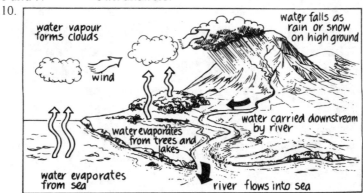

Ice-caps

Question types: 2 literal, 2 inferential, 2 evaluative, 4 deductive
1. The polar regions are at the North and South Poles.
2. The sea has frozen.
3. The sun at the polar regions is not very warm.
4. The warmth of the sun melts the edge of the ice-cap.
5. Own answer.
6. The land above sea-level would get much smaller and change its shape.
7. The ships might run into the icebergs and be badly damaged by them.
8. Own answer.
9. You would freeze to death.
10. An explorer could use melted ice for water.

 Canal locks

Question types: 3 literal, 3 inferential, 3 evaluative, 3 deductive
1. Locks were invented in the 1500s.
2. They were able to sail over hills.
3. A river is a natural waterway and a canal is man-made.
4. Bricks or concrete are used to make the sides and the bottom of the lock.
5. Sluices control the flow of water by opening or shutting.
6. A boat has to wait for the water to get to the right level in a lock.
7–9. Own answers.
10. The gates open and the boat goes into the lock. The lock gates are shut and the sluice opened. The water rises in the lock. The lock gates are opened and the boat leaves the lock.
11. No, the water in a canal does not flow like a river.
12. No, travelling on a canal is a slow way to travel.

Argument

 Homework

Question types: 3 literal, 2 inferential, 2 evaluative, 2 deductive
1. Children need to do homework to be able to learn enough to pass exams.
2. No, not all parents and teachers think homework is a good thing.
3. It helps parents to understand what their children are doing at school.
4. There may be a lot of people in the family and no quiet rooms.
5. The children would make a fuss if they wanted to play or watch TV, or if they felt too tired to concentrate.
6 and 7. Own answers.
8. They need to get into the habit for when they are older and have to work for exams.
9. Own answer.